I'm Going to KINDERGARTEN

Written By: **Kim Mitzo Thompson, Karen Mitzo Hilderbrand**
Executive Producers: **Kim Mitzo Thompson, Karen Mitzo Hilderbrand**
Music Arranged By: **Hal Wright**
Music Vocals: **Nashville Kids Sound**

Learning with music is easy & fun!

Download the 20 songs for **FREE**
from www.downloadkidsmusic.com.

Go to page 3 for the promo code.

1. **The Alphabet Swing**
2. **The Consonant Song**
3. **Learning Our Short Vowels**
4. **Learning Our Long Vowels**
5. **The Silent "e"**
6. **Q And U Are Friends**
7. **Vowel Circuit**
8. **Rhyming Word Rule**
9. **A Little Cat, Cat, Cat**
10. **Jump Rope Rhyme**
11. **Let's Draw Our Shapes**
12. **Counting To Twenty**
13. **I Like To Write, Spell, And Read**
14. **Counting By Tens**
15. **Learning To Add Is Fun**
16. **Just One More**
17. **Call 9-1-1**
18. **Two Is Better Than One**
19. **It's Time To Clean Up**
20. **I Have A Wiggly, Jiggly Tooth**

Published by: Twin Sisters Productions
4710 Hudson Drive
Stow, OH 44224 USA
www.twinsisters.com • 1-800-248-8946

Illustrated by Jackie Binder.

1

DEAR PARENTS & TEACHERS,

This workbook was written to align with The Common Core State Standards to ensure parents and teachers have a clear set of expectations to help children achieve success in and outside of the classroom. Children learn in a variety of ways, and it is my hope that this book is used along with other materials including songs, books, manipulatives, and real-life situations to engage children in the learning process.

According to CoreStandards.org, "The Common Core State Standards Initiative is a state-led effort coordinated by the National Governors Association Center for Best Practices (NGA Center) and the Council of Chief State School Officers (CCSSO). The standards were developed in collaboration with teachers, school administrators, and experts, to provide a clear and consistent framework to prepare our children for college and the workforce."

Currently, the Common Core State Standards are focusing on English-language arts and mathematics for students in grades K-12. As a former classroom teacher, I know the demands put on teachers to individualize instruction and have students meet success, so that they will be prepared for standardized tests. It can be overwhelming. Let's Get Ready For Kindergarten contains a variety of different activities that not only align with the Common Core Standards, but will make learning fun by incorporating songs and rhymes. Download the 20 FREE songs and have your children learn basic skills with music!

Let's work together to ensure all children are well prepared for the future and are given the tools they need for success!

Sincerely,

Kim Mitzo Thompson,
MS Elementary Education

Easily use these learning songs, worksheets, and activities with kids of all learning styles!

Many kids are **visual learners**. They think in pictures, quickly converting everything they read, see, and hear into images in their mind. Most visual learners can sit still at their desk easily, focus for longer periods of time, and turn in neat, organized work. Visual learners are more comfortable learning from workbooks and textbooks.

Other children are **auditory learners**. These kids don't do what visual learners seem to do naturally. Auditory learners learn best by listening —being read to, listening to audio books, discussing a topic one-on-one with a teacher or within a small group, singing and learning with music and rhythm.

Still other children are **kinesthetic learners** who learn best through a hands-on approach, body movement, activities, arts and crafts, and manipulating objects.

These songs, worksheets and activities are easily adaptable for use both at home or in the classroom. Parents and caregivers may jumpstart or reinforce school learning at home with the fun, family activities. Classroom teachers may adapt the activities and worksheets as a supplement to their curriculum.

Download the 20 songs for **FREE** from
www.downloadkidsmusic.com.
Enter Promo Code: JB279K

COMMON CORE STANDARDS

The Common Core Standards covered in this workbook.

READING AND LANGUAGE ARTS

Reading Foundational Skills RF.K.1

Demonstrate understanding of the organization and basic features of print.
- Follow words from left to right, top to bottom, and page by page.
- Recognize that spoken words are represented in written language by specific sequence of letters.
- Understand that words are separated by spaces in print.
- Recognize and name all upper and lowercase letters of the alphabet.

Reading Foundational Skills RF.K.2

Demonstrate understanding of spoken words and sounds.
- Recognize and produce rhyming words.
- Isolate and pronounce the initial, medial vowel, and final sounds in (consonant-vowel-consonant, or CVC) words.
- Add or substitute individual sounds in simple, one-syllable words to make new words.

Reading Foundational Skills RF.K.3

Know and apply grade-level phonics and word analysis skills in decoding words.
- Demonstrate basic knowledge of letter-sound correspondences by producing the primary or most frequent sound for each consonant.
- Associate the long and short sounds with the common spellings for the five major vowels.

Reading Foundational Skills RF.K.4

Read emergent-reader texts with purpose and understanding.

English Language Arts / Writing W.K.2

Use a combination of drawing, dictating, and writing to compose informative/explanatory texts in which they name what they are writing about and supply some information about the topic.

English Language Arts / Language L.K.1

Demonstrate command of the conventions of standard English grammar and usage when writing or speaking.
- Print many upper- and lowercase letters.

The Letter Dd

Trace and write the uppercase letter **D**.

D

Trace and write the lowercase letter **d**.

d

Nn Oo Pp Qq Rr Ss Tt Uu Vv Ww Xx Yy Zz

Circle each picture whose name begins with **d**.

The Letter Ee

Trace and write the uppercase letter **E**.

Trace and write the lowercase letter **e**.

Aa Bb Cc Dd **Ee** Ff Gg Hh Ii Jj Kk Ll Mm

Circle each picture whose name begins with e.

The Letter Ff

Trace and write the uppercase letter **F**.

Trace and write the lowercase letter **f**.

Circle each picture whose name begins with **f**.

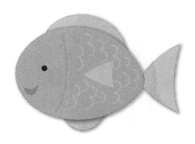

The Letter Gg

Trace and write the uppercase letter G.

Trace and write the lowercase letter g.

Aa Bb Cc Dd Ee Ff Gg Hh Ii Jj Kk Ll Mm

Circle each picture whose name begins with g.

The Letter Hh

Trace and write the uppercase letter **H**.

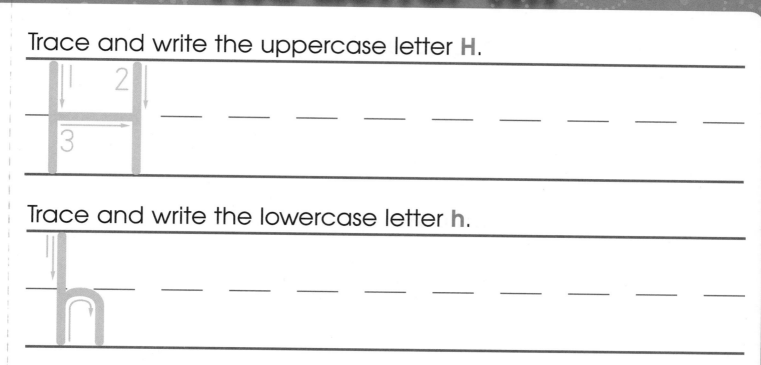

Trace and write the lowercase letter **h**.

Nn Oo Pp Qq Rr Ss Tt Uu Vv Ww Xx Yy Zz

Circle each picture whose name begins with h.

The Letter Ii

Trace and write the uppercase letter I.

Trace and write the lowercase letter i.

Aa Bb Cc Dd Ee Ff Gg Hh Ii Jj Kk Ll Mm

Circle each picture whose name begins with i.

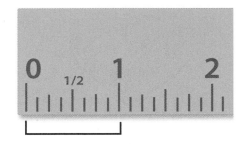

The Letter Jj

Trace and write the uppercase letter J.

J

Trace and write the lowercase letter j.

j

Nn Oo Pp Qq Rr Ss Tt Uu Vv Ww Xx Yy Zz

Circle each picture whose name begins with j.

The Letter Kk

Trace and write the uppercase letter **K**.

K

Trace and write the lowercase letter **k**.

k

Aa Bb Cc Dd Ee Ff Gg Hh Ii Jj Kk Ll Mm

Circle each picture whose name begins with **k**.

The Letter Ll

Trace and write the uppercase letter **L**.

Trace and write the lowercase letter **l**.

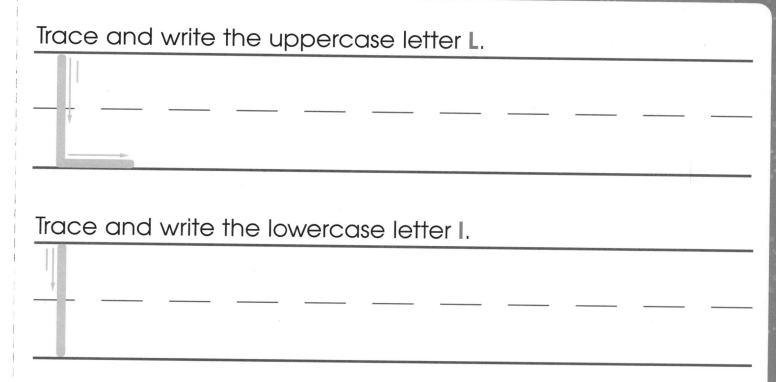

Circle each picture whose name begins with **l**.

The Letter Mm

Trace and write the uppercase letter **M**.

Trace and write the lowercase letter **m**.

Aa Bb Cc Dd Ee Ff Gg Hh Ii Jj Kk Ll Mm

Circle each picture whose name begins with **m**.

The Letter Nn

Trace and write the uppercase letter **N**.

Trace and write the lowercase letter **n**.

Nn Oo Pp Qq Rr Ss Tt Uu Vv Ww Xx Yy Zz

Circle each picture whose name begins with **n**.

The Letter Oo

Trace and write the uppercase letter O.

Trace and write the lowercase letter o.

Aa Bb Cc Dd Ee Ff Gg Hh Ii Jj Kk Ll Mm

Circle each picture whose name begins with o.

The Letter Pp

Trace and write the uppercase letter **P**.

P

Trace and write the lowercase letter **p**.

p

Nn Oo Pp Qq Rr Ss Tt Uu Vv Ww Xx Yy Zz

Circle each picture whose name begins with **p**.

21

The Letter Qq

Trace and write the uppercase letter **Q**.

Trace and write the lowercase letter **q**.

Aa Bb Cc Dd Ee Ff Gg Hh Ii Jj Kk Ll Mm

Circle each picture whose name begins with q.

The Letter Rr

Trace and write the uppercase letter **R**.

Trace and write the lowercase letter **r**.

Circle each picture whose name begins with **r**.

23

The Letter Ss

Trace and write the uppercase letter **S**.

S

Trace and write the lowercase letter **s**.

s

Aa Bb Cc Dd Ee Ff Gg Hh Ii Jj Kk Ll Mm

Circle each picture whose name begins with **s**.

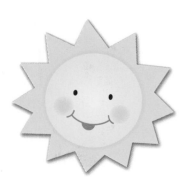

The Letter Tt

Trace and write the uppercase letter T.

Trace and write the lowercase letter t.

Nn Oo Pp Qq Rr Ss Tt Uu Vv Ww Xx Yy Zz

Circle each picture whose name begins with t.

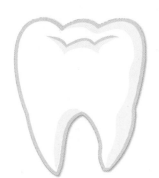

25

The Letter Uu

Trace and write the uppercase letter **U**.

Trace and write the lowercase letter **u**.

Aa Bb Cc Dd Ee Ff Gg Hh Ii Jj Kk Ll Mm

Circle each picture whose name begins with u.

The Letter Vv

Trace and write the uppercase letter **V**.

Trace and write the lowercase letter **v**.

Nn Oo Pp Qq Rr Ss Tt Uu Vv Ww Xx Yy Zz

Circle each picture whose name begins with **v**.

The Letter Ww

Trace and write the uppercase letter **W**.

Trace and write the lowercase letter **w**.

Circle each picture whose name begins with **w**.

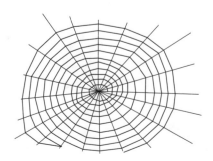

The Letter Xx

Trace and write the uppercase letter **X**.

Trace and write the lowercase letter **x**.

Did you know that the letter **x** is usually heard at the end of a word? It makes the /**ks**/ sound like in **box** or **fox**. Say these words aloud: **six**, **mix**, **fix**.

Nn Oo Pp Qq Rr Ss Tt Uu Vv Ww Xx Yy Zz

Circle the pictures that end with the **x** sound.

The Letter Yy

Trace and write the uppercase letter **Y**.

Trace and write the lowercase letter **y**.

Aa Bb Cc Dd Ee Ff Gg Hh Ii Jj Kk Ll Mm

Circle each picture whose name begins with **y**.

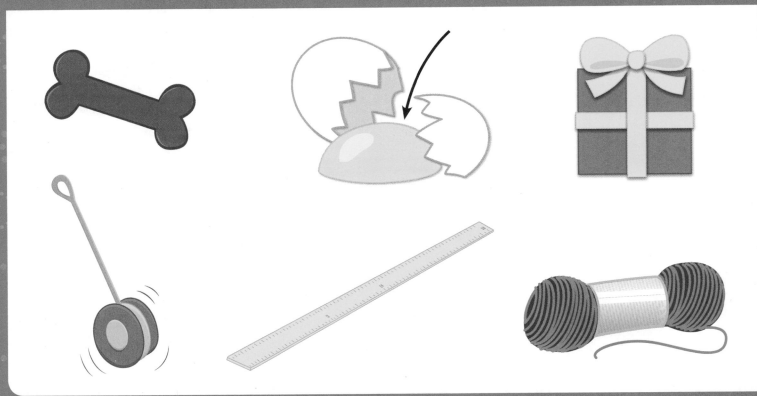

The Letter Zz

Trace and write the uppercase letter **Z**.

Z

Trace and write the lowercase letter **z**.

z

Nn Oo Pp Qq Rr Ss Tt Uu Vv Ww Xx Yy Zz

Circle each picture whose name begins with **z**.

Letter Partners

Draw a line to match each uppercase letter to its lowercase letter partner.

B

N

Y

A

E

K

Q

k

a

e

q

b

y

n

Letter Partners

Draw a line to match each uppercase letter to its lowercase letter partner.

G

M

Q

H

P

J

Y

h

p

j

y

q

m

g

Letter Partners

Write each lowercase letter next to the uppercase letter.

T	

W	

R	

B	

P	

M	

A	

E	

e t a b w p r m

Letter Partners

Write each uppercase letter next to the lowercase letter.

d	

i	

k	

q	

x	

f	

g	

n	

N I K X G Q D F

Beginning Sounds

Name each picture. Circle the letter for its beginning sound.

k d o		n h s
g e f		y b d
a z g		v l w
a t c		v t e

Beginning Sounds

Name each picture. Circle the letter for its beginning sound.

k d a			n f s
g e f			g b d
a c l			y w f
a c z			k h w

Beginning Sounds

Name each picture. Circle the letter for its beginning sound.

k r o		n h s
g e t	**2**	a b d
u z g		v f w
a h c		c l w

Beginning Sounds

Name each picture. Circle the letter for its beginning sound.

k w h			n h s
d e f			o r d
a z g			a z b
a t c			s l w

Beginning Sounds

Name each picture. Circle the letter for its beginning sound.

l
r
o

a
h
s

g
e
t

a
b
q

u
z
c

a
b
q

v
f
w

s
j
h

c
l
z

Beginning Sounds

Name each picture. Circle the letter for its beginning sound.

j w h			n h z
b e f			o r d
a h g			f z b
a z l			i c w

Beginning Sounds

Name each picture. Circle the letter for its beginning sound.

r
m
o

b
h
s

g
y
t

a
x
w

h
z
s

v
f
e

c
j
h

c
r
z

Beginning Sounds

Name each picture. Circle the letter for its beginning sound.

b
m
o

a
r
s

z
e
d

a
n
w

u
f
s

v
t
e

c
p
h

o
l
z

Beginning Sounds

Name each picture. Circle the letter for its beginning sound.

j
r
h

n
b
z

b
i
f

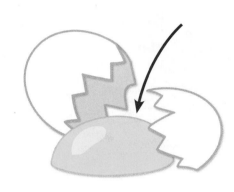

o
y
d

a
h
g

f
z
b

a
b
c

2 4 9
3 8 10

i
l
n

Beginning Sounds

Name each picture. Circle the letter for its beginning sound.

k
m
o

a
h
b

z
g
d

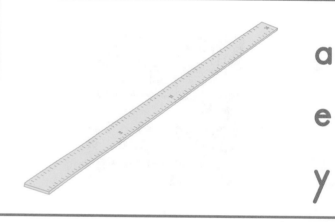

a
e
y

y
f
b

v
h
e

c
j
k

o
l
z

Beginning Sounds

Name each picture. Circle the letter for its beginning sound.

j
p
l

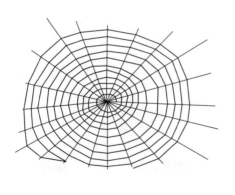

n
d
z

q
e
f

j
y
d

a
w
g

f
k
b

f
z
c

i
p
n

Beginning Sounds

Name each picture. Circle the letter for its beginning sound.

b
n
o

a
h
c

z
c
q

a
e
p

u
f
b

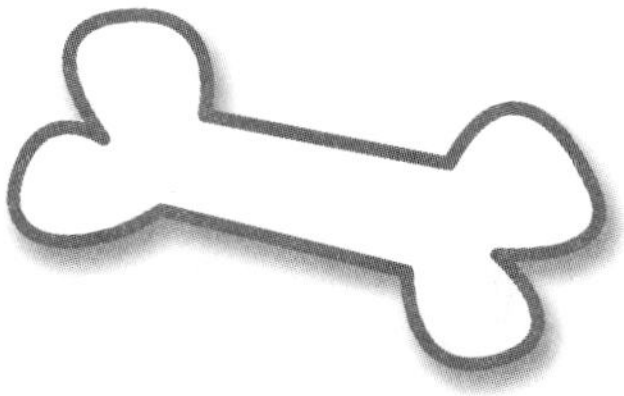

v
h
e

c
w
k

r
l
z

Beginning Sounds

Name each picture. Circle the letter for its beginning sound.

x
f
h

n
b
z

q
m
f

j
p
d

a
w
o

f
k
s

b
h
c

i
l
n

Beginning Sounds

Name each picture. Circle the letter for its beginning sound.

x
f
h

n
d
c

q
a
k

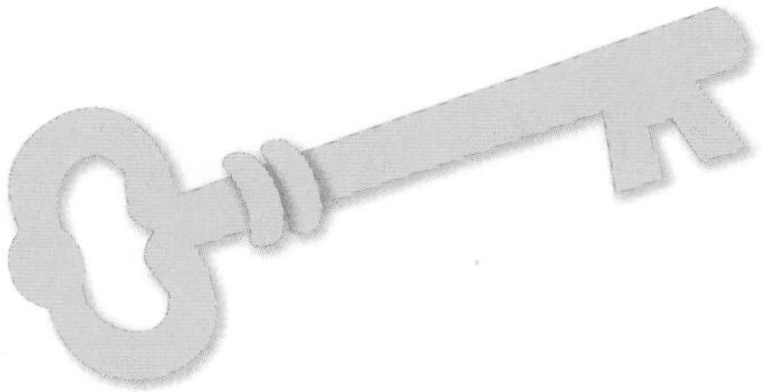

j
p
d

a
w
o

f
k
b

d
z
c

i
m
l

Learning About Short a

Cat has the short sound of **a**. Color the pictures that have the **short a** sound.

Reading Words

Look at each picture. Write a short **a** to complete each word.

b___g	c___t
l___mp	b___t
c___n	h___t

Learning About Short e

Bed has the short sound of **e**. Color the pictures that have the **short e** sound.

Reading Words

Look at each picture. Write a short **e** to complete each word.

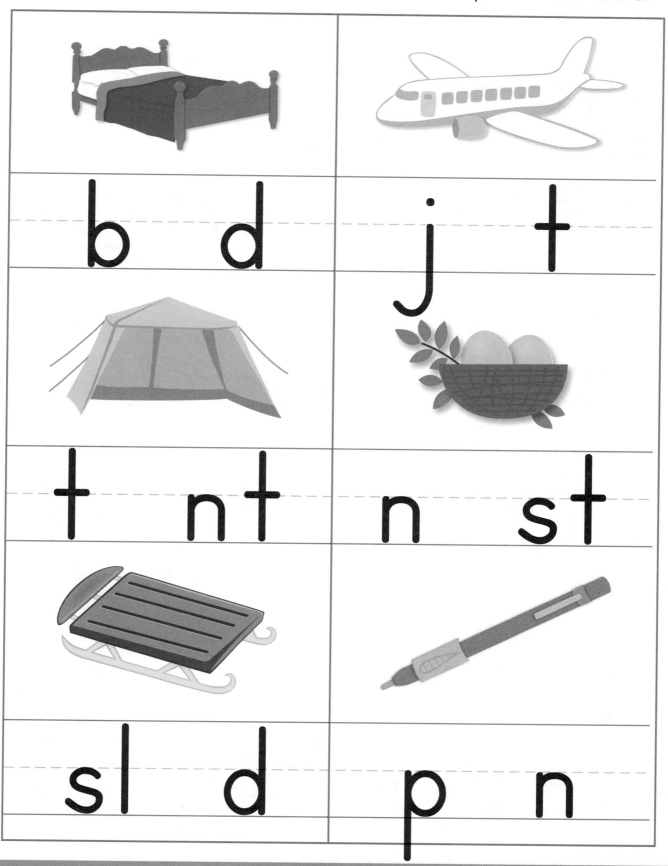

b ___ d   j ___ t

t ___ n t   n ___ s t

s l ___ d   p ___ n

Learning About Short i

Bib has the short sound of **i**. Color the pictures that have the **short i** sound.

Reading Words

Look at each picture. Write a short **i** to complete each word.

f __ sh	p __ g
s __ x	m __ lk
d __ sh	l __ ps

Learning About Short o

Mop has the short sound of o. Color the pictures that have the **short o** sound.

Reading Words

Look at each picture. Write a short **o** to complete each word.

s _ ck

fr _ g

d _ g

m _ p

b _ x

f _ x

Learning About Short u

Bus has the short sound of **u**. Color the pictures that have the **short u** sound.

PHONICS SCHOOL

Reading Words

Look at each picture. Write a short **u** to complete each word.

c ___ p   r ___ g

b ___ g   s ___ n

d ___ ck   sk ___ nk

Short Vowel Review

Look at each picture. **Circle** the correct **short vowel**.

a u o

o e u

a i e

i o u

a e u

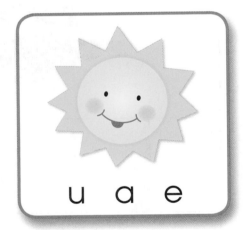

u a e

a u i

a i e

Short Vowel Review

Look at each picture. **Circle** the correct **short vowel**.

i a e

a e i

u a e

i a u

e a i

o u a

a u o

o a e

Write the Missing Vowel

Look at each picture. **Write** the **missing vowel** in each blank. Say each word.

f _ sh

s _ ck

c _ p

s _ x

b _ d

n _ st

b _ g

f _ x

Write the Missing Vowel

Look at each picture. **Write** the **missing vowel** in each blank. Say each word.

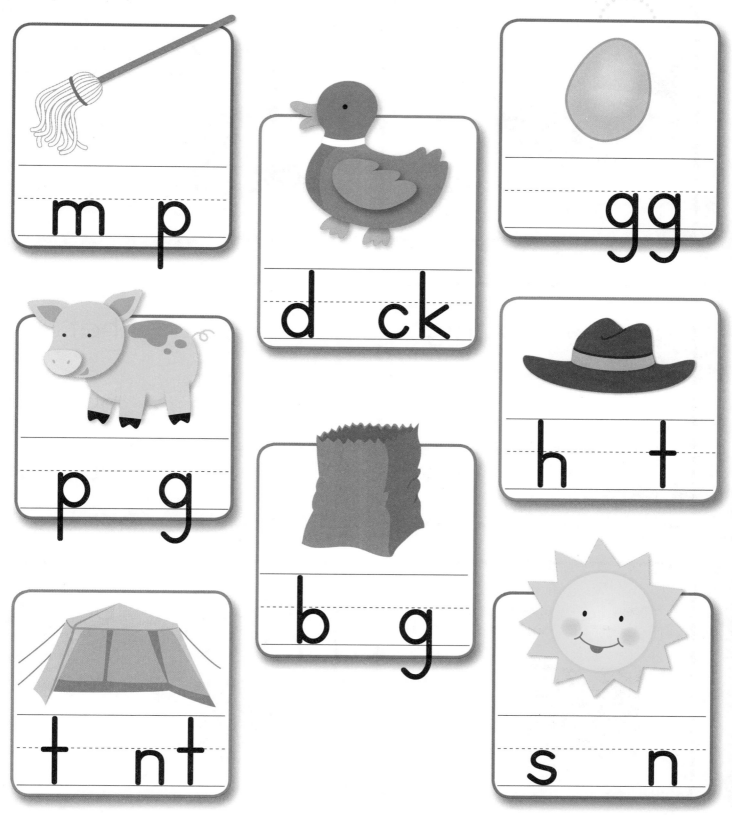

m _ p

d _ ck

_ gg

p _ g

b _ g

h _ t

t _ nt

s _ n

Circle the short Vowel Word

Circle the word for each picture.

bag

bed

deb

bip

dig

bib

pig

pan

pen

hat

hand

hop

dig

drum

fun

box

frog

fox

Circle the short Vowel Word

Circle the word for each picture.

can

cup

bag

beg

bag

big

stop

man

mop

fish

dish

find

big

bag

bell

ten

men

pen

The Matching Game

Draw a line from each picture to its matching word.

mop

dish

nest

sock

The Matching Game

Draw **a line** from each picture to its matching word.

bag

hat

mitt

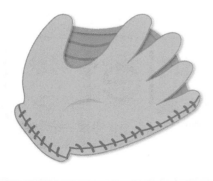

duck

The Matching Game

Draw a line from each picture to its matching word.

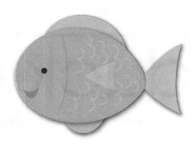

bat

fish

bus

jet

The Matching Game

Draw a line from each picture to its matching word.

dog

fox

bed

frog

Silent e

When you see the letter **e** at the end of a word it will make the vowel say its name. The letter **e** will not make any sound.

 becomes

 becomes

Practice saying these words.

short vowel sound	long vowel sound
mad	made
pan	pane
rat	rate
tap	tape
bit	bite
dim	dime
fin	fine
kit	kite
pin	pine
rip	ripe
hop	hope
not	note
rob	robe
tub	tube

Long Vowel ā

Unscramble the words and write them on the line.
Look at the word box to help you.

tlepa	nskae
cfea	ncea
agte	ckae

cake   plate   snake
gate   cane   face

Long Vowel ī

Unscramble the words and write them on the line.
Look at the word box to help you.

cmei	nnei
keit	beki
mied	vfie

bike	mice	dime
nine	five	kite

Long Vowel ō

Unscramble the words and write them on the line.
Look at the word box to help you.

snoe	**peor**
obne	**moeh**
sroe	**tnoe**

bone	nose	rope
note	home	rose

Long Vowels With Silent e

Say the name of each picture.
Write the correct long vowel in the blank.

a

Long Vowels With Silent e

Say the name of each picture.
Write the correct long vowel in the blank.

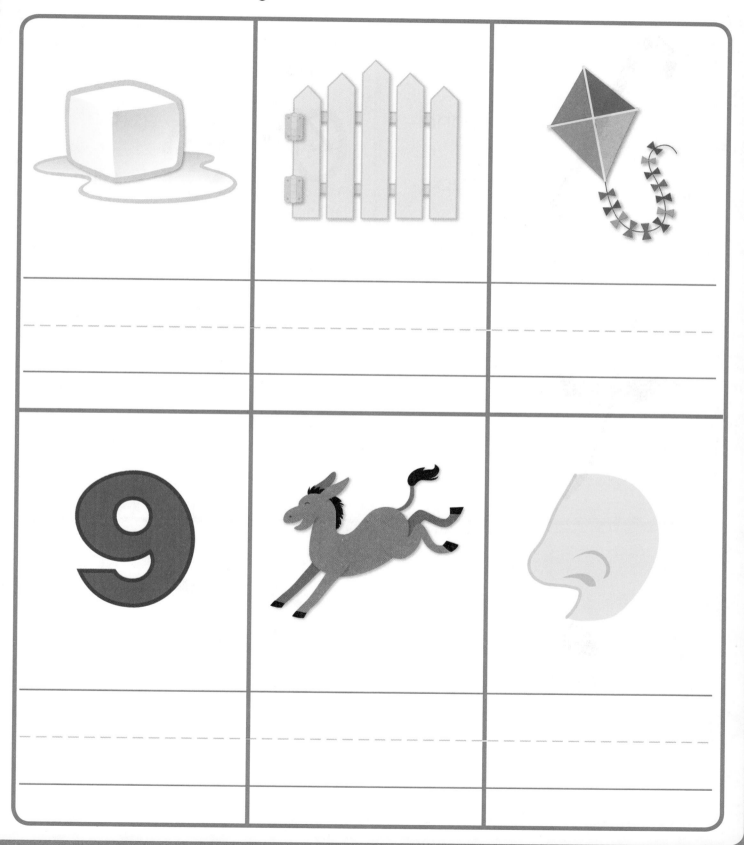

Long Vowels

Cirlce the correct word for each picture.

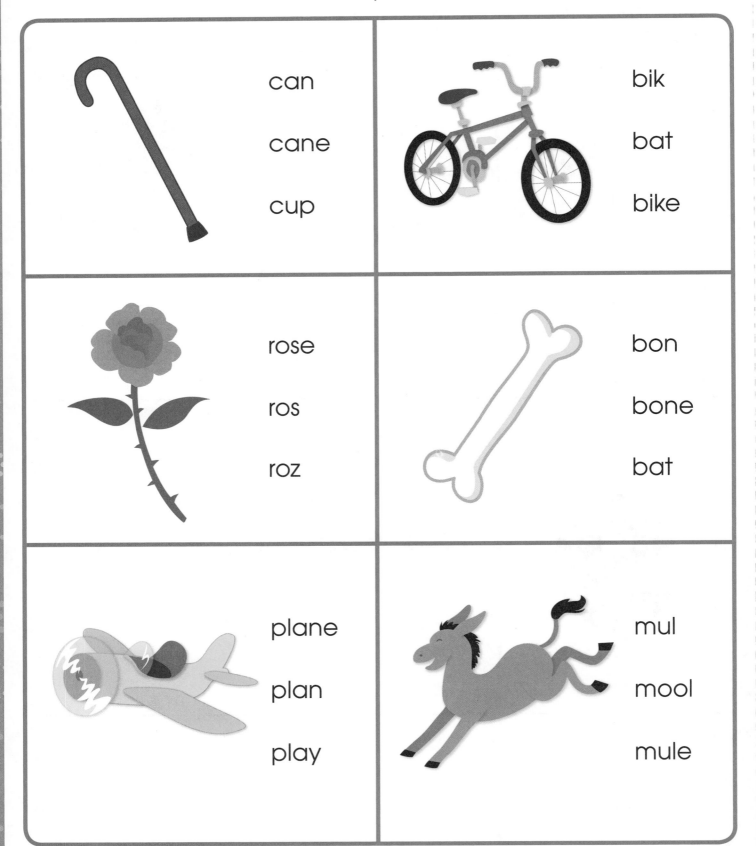

can cane cup	bik bat bike
rose ros roz	bon bone bat
plane plan play	mul mool mule

Long Vowels

Cirlce the correct word for each picture.

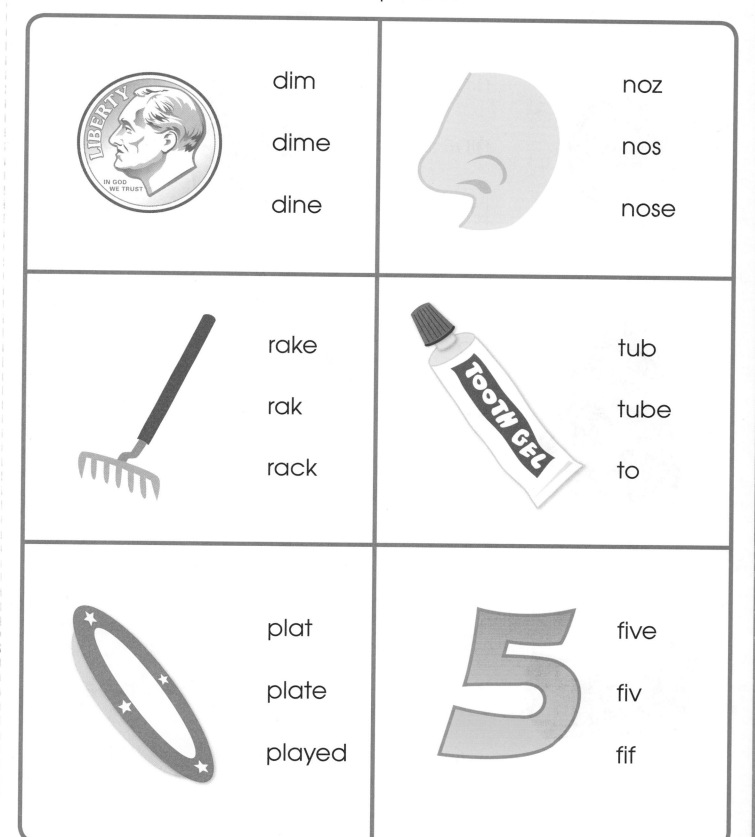

dim dime dine	noz nos nose
rake rak rack	tub tube to
plat plate played	five fiv fif

Long Vowels

Cirlce the correct word for each picture.

nin

nine

nim

rope

rop

roe

ap

ape

a

snake

snak

snack

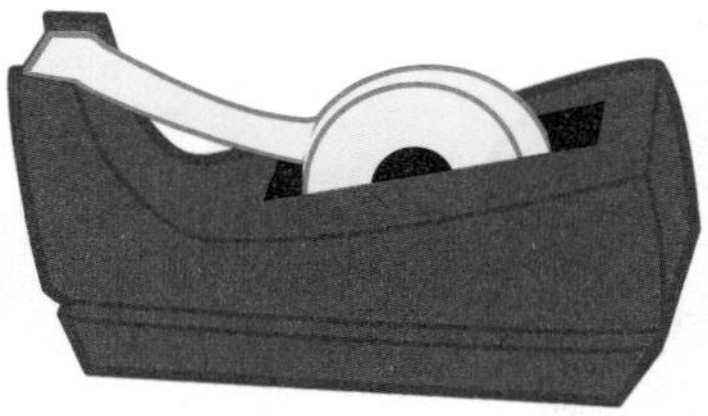

tape

tupe

tap

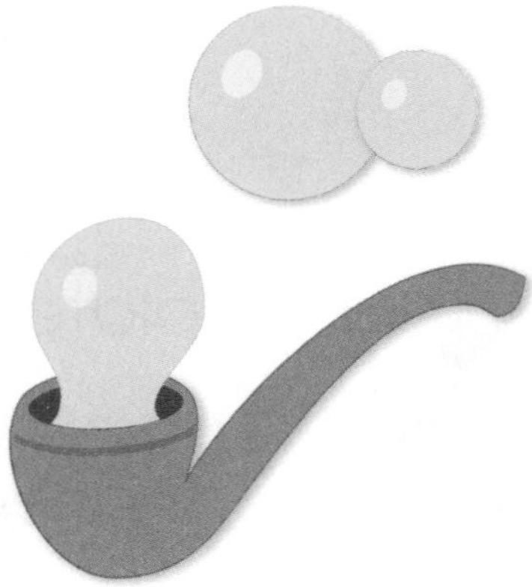

pip

pipe

pib

Long Vowels

Cirlce the correct word for each picture.

not
no
note

page
pag
pa

cub
cube
coob

mice
mic
miss

hug
hage
huge

bite
bit
bet

Learning Sight Words

Sight words are words that a reader should recognize instantly. Most of these words are not decodable - you can't sound them out. Children who learn these words are well on their way to becoming successful readers.

The following sight words will be introduced in this workbook on pages 82-115. Use the sight word flash cards for additional practice. Make learning fun by using some of our suggested activities.

a	all	am	and
are	at	big	can
can't	come	do	for
get	go	had	has
have	he	here	his
is	it	like	little
live	look	lots	me
my	on	one	said
see	she	that	the
there	they	this	to
up	want	was	we
went	what	where	who
why	will	with	you

Hands-On Phonics Activities

I SPY

Place several objects on a tray—for example, use a button, sock, candle, bone, and rock. If necessary, identify each object. Now say, "I spy something on the tray that begins with the sound of the letter **s**." Your child finds the sock, picks it up and says, "sock!" For more challenging play, ask your child to close his eyes while you remove an object from the tray. Ask him to open his eyes, identify the missing object and name the letter that makes its beginning sound.

MIRROR, MIRROR

Help your child think of words that begin with the sound of a selected letter. Ask your child to repeat those words several times while looking in a mirror. Observe if the mouth positioning is the same for each letter sound. Ask your child to repeat various words several times while looking in a mirror. Help your child notice whether or not her lips touched when she said the beginning sound. Was the tongue touching her front teeth or the roof of her mouth?

BEGINNING SOUND GUESSING GAME

Play a beginning sound guessing game throughout the day. In the morning say, "Please put on something that begins like the word umbrella." (Answer: underwear.) "Now, I want you to put on something that begins like the word sheep." (Answer: shirt.) During lunch you might say, "We're making sandwiches. Please bring me something we'll need that begins like the word brown." (Answer: bread.) Before leaving the house you might say, "We'll need to take something that begins like the word king." (Answer: keys.) In the evening say, "Please turn off the item that begins like the word top." (Answer: television.)

WHERE IS IT?

Use this activity while waiting at a restaurant or in the doctor's office to help your child differentiate sound position in words. Draw three boxes, connected horizontally, on a sheet of paper. Use a coin or piece of candy as a marker. Explain that you are going to say words that have a certain sound. The sound may be at the beginning, in the middle, or at the end of the word. If the sound is at the beginning of the word, your child places a marker in the first box. If the sound is in the middle, your child places a marker in the second box. If the sound is at the end of the word, your child places a marker in the last box.

TEACHERS:

Copy this page and give to parents at conferences to help reinforce what you are teaching at school.

Trace and write each word.

the

big

is

Circle the sight words in the puzzle below.
How many can you find?

i	b	r	j	t	e	b
s	m	i	n	h	y	i
t	h	e	g	e	d	g
k	a	i	t	l	s	l
b	i	g	s	h	v	i
z	w	t	h	e	e	s

Sight Words

the   **big**   **is**

Write the correct word to complete the sentence.

Is _____ dog little?

The dog is _____.

The dog _____ brown.

Write your own sentence using one or more of the sight words above. Remember to use a capital letter to begin your sentence. Use a punctuation mark to end your sentence.

_____

_____

_____

Sight Words

Trace and write each word.

at   a

me

you

Circle the sight words in the puzzle below.
How many can you find?

y	a	n	a	t	m	y
v	o	t	s	c	e	o
b	y	u	p	a	i	u
m	e	d	m	e	z	p
t	a	n	a	h	m	e
y	o	u	j	g	a	t

Sight Words

at   a   me   you

Write the correct word to complete the sentence.

Will _____ play with _____ ?

I am _____ school.

I have _____ ball.

Write your own sentence using one or more of the sight words above. Remember to use a capital letter to begin your sentence. Use a punctuation mark to end your sentence.

_____

_____

_____

_____

Sight Words

Trace and write each word.

my

has

she

Circle the sight words in the puzzle below.
How many can you find?

m	y	z	w	j	s	h
h	j	e	m	y	h	a
s	a	a	b	m	e	s
n	h	s	y	t	y	r
i	q	e	m	s	h	e
h	a	s	y	h	a	s

Sight Words

my   **has**   **she**

Write the correct word to complete the sentence.

I like _____ cat.

She _____ black fur.

Is _____ little?

Write your own sentence using one or more of the sight words above. Remember to use a capital letter to begin your sentence. Use a punctuation mark to end your sentence.

_____

_____

_____

_____

Sight Words

Trace and write each word.

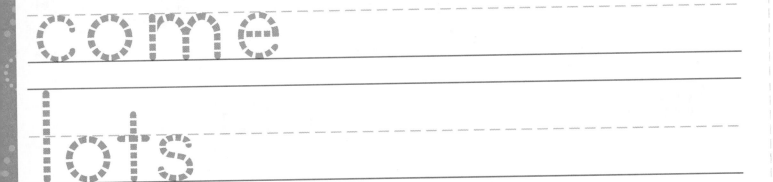

come

lots

can

Circle the sight words in the puzzle below.
How many can you find?

c	o	m	e	g	l	c
c	l	c	a	n	o	o
a	d	o	y	r	t	m
n	r	z	t	w	s	e
l	o	t	s	s	m	q
c	o	m	e	c	a	n

Sight Words

Write the correct word to complete the sentence.

Will you _____ over?

I have _____ of toys.

Yes, I _____.

Write your own sentence using one or more of the sight words above. Remember to use a capital letter to begin your sentence. Use a punctuation mark to end your sentence.

_____

_____

_____

Sight Words

Trace and write each word.

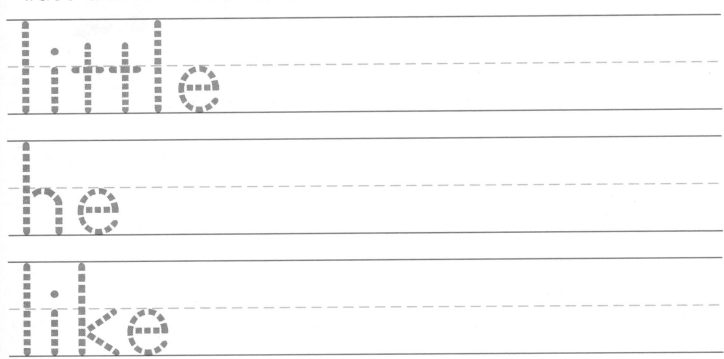

little

he

like

Circle the sight words in the puzzle below.
How many can you find?

l	r	l	i	k	e	o
i	l	i	t	t	l	e
t	o	h	e	b	h	e
t	l	i	k	e	m	c
l	h	e	l	i	k	e
e	e	l	i	t	t	l	e

Sight Words

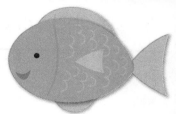

little   He   like

Write the correct word to complete the sentence.

My fish is _____ .

Do you _____ him?

_____ is red.

Write your own sentence using one or more of the sight words above. Remember to use a capital letter to begin your sentence. Use a punctuation mark to end your sentence.

_____

_____

_____

Sight Words

Trace and write each word.

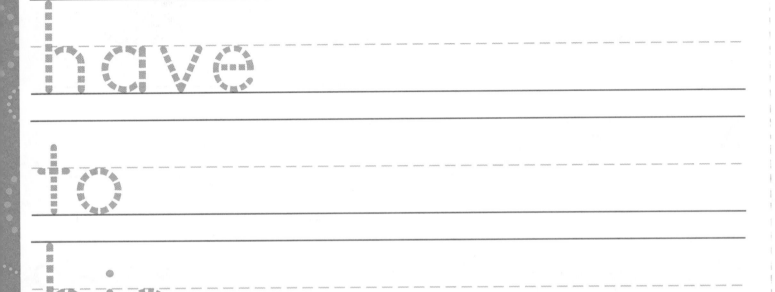

have

to

his

Circle the sight words in the puzzle below.
How many can you find?

h	t	o	h	y	a	h
z	a	m	r	i	n	a
h	t	v	q	x	s	v
i	e	o	e	t	o	e
s	k	b	w	h	i	s
h	a	v	e	l	t	o

Sight Words

have to His

Write the correct word to complete the sentence.

I _____ a black dog.

He likes _____ play ball.

_____ name is Pete.

Write your own sentence using one or more of the sight words above. Remember to use a capital letter to begin your sentence. Use a punctuation mark to end your sentence.

_____

_____

_____

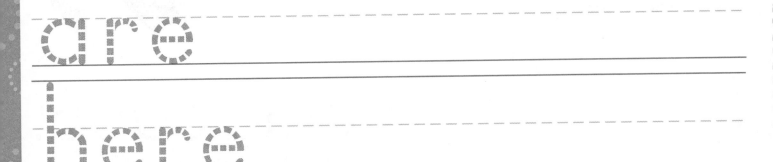

Sight Words

Trace and write each word.

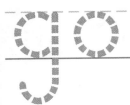

are

here

go

Circle the sight words in the puzzle below.
How many can you find?

h	y	a	r	e	u	h
n	e	q	g	o	b	e
j	l	r	m	h	a	r
a	r	e	e	c	r	e
g	o	a	r	e	e	s
h	e	r	e	l	g	o

Sight Words

Are   Here   go

Write the correct word to complete the sentence.

_____ you cold?

_____ is a coat.

Now you can _____ outside.

Write your own sentence using one or more of the sight words above. Remember to use a capital letter to begin your sentence. Use a punctuation mark to end your sentence.

_____

_____

_____

Sight Words

Trace and write each word.

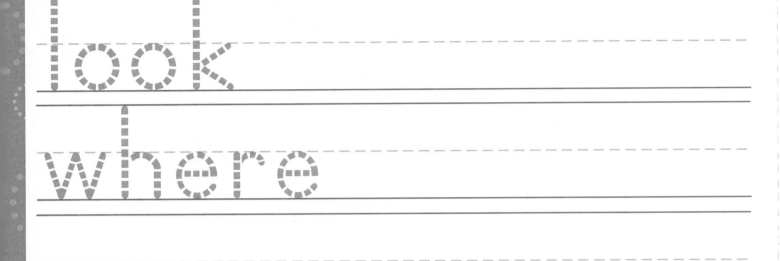

Circle the sight words in the puzzle below.
How many can you find?

w	w	h	e	r	e	l
h	l	l	o	o	k	o
e	u	o	t	u	p	o
r	p	v	o	j	m	k
e	s	u	p	k	g	u
n	w	h	e	r	e	p

Sight Words

Look   Where   up

Write the correct word to complete the sentence.

_____ at the bird.

_____ is the bird?

It is _____ in the tree.

Write your own sentence using one or more of the sight words above. Remember to use a capital letter to begin your sentence. Use a punctuation mark to end your sentence.

_____

_____

_____

Sight Words

Trace and write each word.

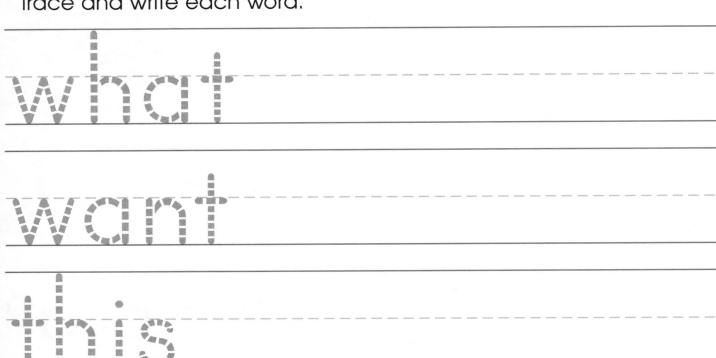

Circle the sight words in the puzzle below.
How many can you find?

w	t	w	a	n	t	t
h	h	v	l	w	x	h
a	i	w	a	n	t	i
t	s	t	h	i	s	s
n	m	e	w	a	n	t
w	h	a	t	r	p	z

Sight Words

What   want   this

Write the correct word to complete the sentence.

_____ do you want to eat?

I _____ a pear.

I want _____ one.

Write your own sentence using one or more of the sight words above. Remember to use a capital letter to begin your sentence. Use a punctuation mark to end your sentence.

_____

_____

_____

_____

Sight Words

Trace and write each word.

said

will

we

Circle the sight words in the puzzle below.
How many can you find?

s	w	i	l	l	l	w	s
k	a	r	w	e	i	a
w	j	i	o	s	l	i
e	z	q	d	w	l	d
w	i	l	l	e	p	m
s	a	i	d	n	w	e

Sight Words

said   **Will**   **We**

Write the correct word to complete the sentence.

My mom _____ to come inside.

_____ live in the white house.

_____ you come over?

Write your own sentence using one or more of the sight words above. Remember to use a capital letter to begin your sentence. Use a punctuation mark to end your sentence.

_____

_____

_____

Sight Words

Trace and write each word.

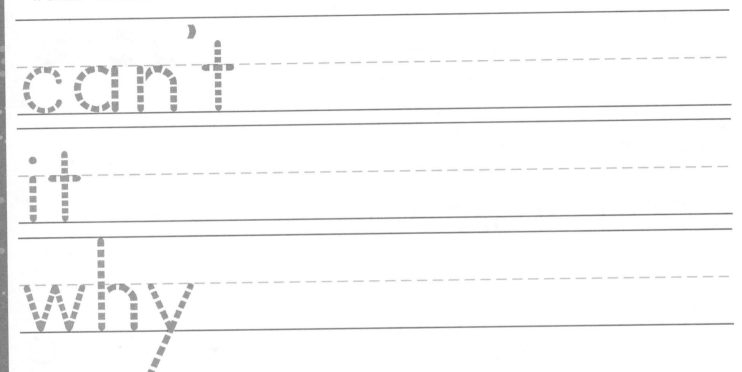

can't

it

why

Circle the sight words in the puzzle below.
How many can you find?

c	w	h	y	c	w	c
b	a	i	t	a	h	a
w	e	n	y	n	y	n
l	h	j	't	't	p	't
i	t	y	s	o	i	t
c	a	n	't	w	h	y

Sight Words

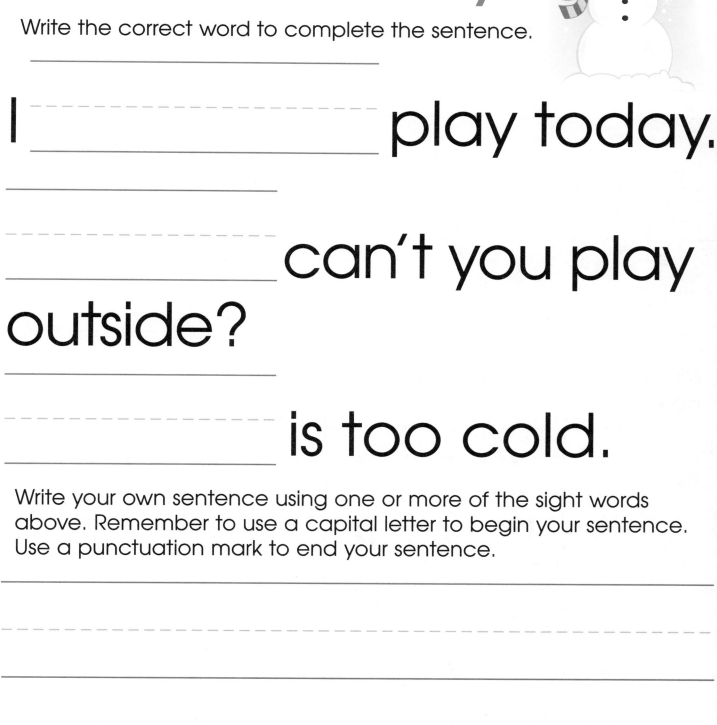

can't   It   Why

Write the correct word to complete the sentence.

I _____ play today.

_____ can't you play outside?

_____ is too cold.

Write your own sentence using one or more of the sight words above. Remember to use a capital letter to begin your sentence. Use a punctuation mark to end your sentence.

_____

_____

_____

Sight Words

Trace and write each word.

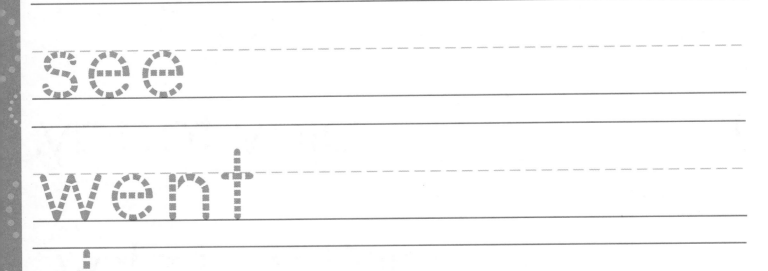

see

went

there

Circle the sight words in the puzzle below.
How many can you find?

t	w	e	n	t	w	t
s	h	r	p	s	e	h
e	z	e	m	e	n	e
e	k	h	r	e	t	r
w	e	n	t	e	o	e
t	h	e	r	e	n	l

Sight Words

see　　**went**　　**there**

Write the correct word to complete the sentence.

I _____ a pink pig.

It _____ in the pen.

The pen is over _____.

Write your own sentence using one or more of the sight words above. Remember to use a capital letter to begin your sentence. Use a punctuation mark to end your sentence.

_____

_____

_____

Sight Words

Trace and write each word.

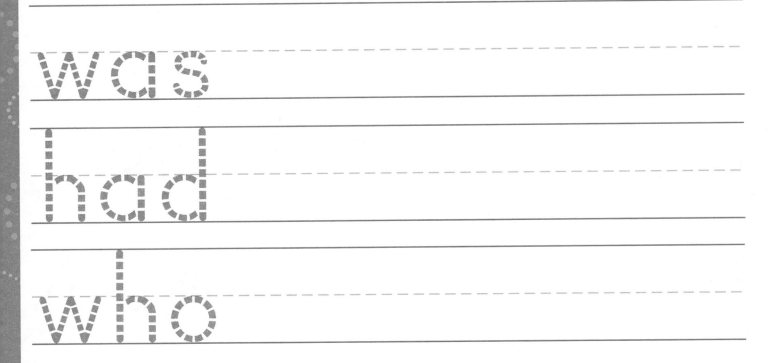

was

had

who

Circle the sight words in the puzzle below.
How many can you find?

w	o	w	t	e	w	h
m	a	a	w	b	a	a
y	x	s	h	o	s	d
h	a	d	o	h	a	d
w	h	o	m	w	h	o
r	w	a	d	h	a	d

Sight Words

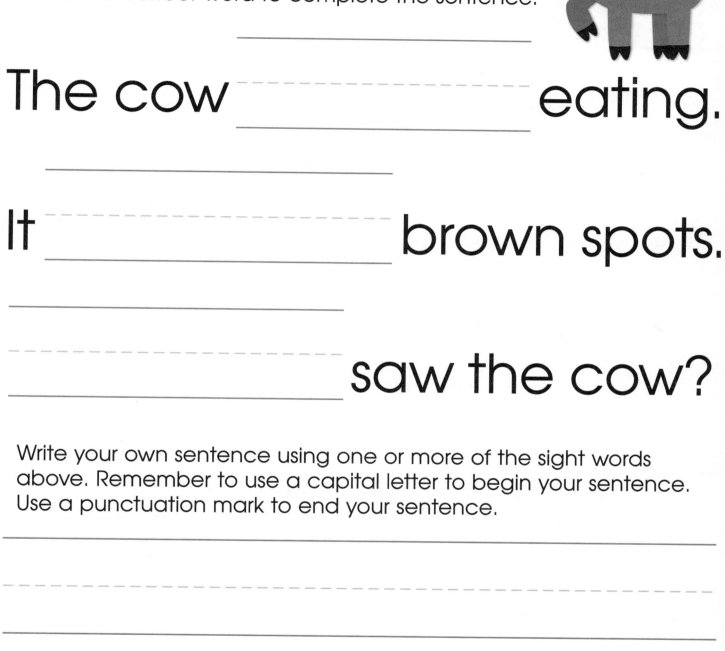

was   had   Who

Write the correct word to complete the sentence.

The cow _____ eating.

It _____ brown spots.

_____ saw the cow?

Write your own sentence using one or more of the sight words above. Remember to use a capital letter to begin your sentence. Use a punctuation mark to end your sentence.

_____

_____

_____

Sight Words

Trace and write each word.

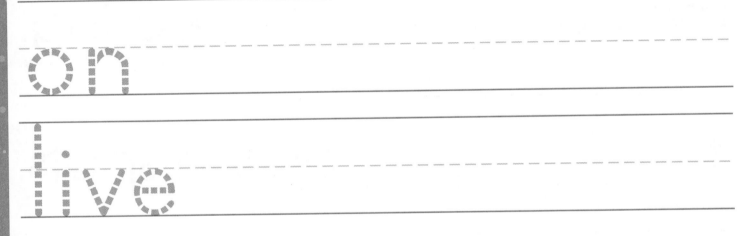

that

on

live

Circle the sight words in the puzzle below.
How many can you find?

t	s	t	h	a	t	t
o	n	o	n	l	l	h
n	k	a	r	i	i	a
e	o	n	t	v	v	t
l	i	v	e	e	e	a
m	t	h	a	t	o	n

Sight Words

That   on   live

Write the correct word to complete the sentence.

_____ frog is green.

He is _____ the leaf.

Where does he _____?

Write your own sentence using one or more of the sight words above. Remember to use a capital letter to begin your sentence. Use a punctuation mark to end your sentence.

_____

_____

_____

Sight Words

Trace and write each word.

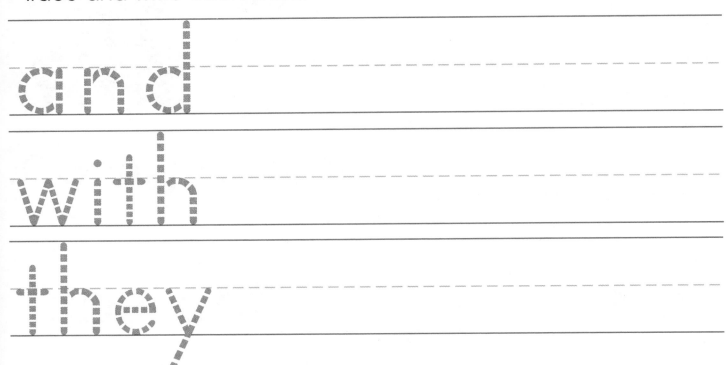

and

with

they

Circle the sight words in the puzzle below.
How many can you find?

r	w	a	m	a	u	t
t	c	i	l	n	f	h
h	k	w	t	d	o	e
e	a	n	d	h	a	y
y	w	i	t	h	n	l
r	t	h	e	y	d	o

Sight Words

and　　　　**with**　　　　**They**

Write the correct word to complete the sentence.

The cat _____ dog are pets.

They play _____ toys.

_____ live in my house.

Write your own sentence using one or more of the sight words above. Remember to use a capital letter to begin your sentence. Use a punctuation mark to end your sentence.

_____

_____

_____

_____

Sight Words

Trace and write each word.

do

for

one

Circle the sight words in the puzzle below.
How many can you find?

o	s	f	d	o	f	o
o	n	m	o	l	o	n
h	n	e	s	r	r	e
o	a	e	d	o	d	o
n	o	n	e	f	o	r
e	r	f	o	r	d	o

Sight Words

Do for one

Write the correct word to complete the sentence.

_____ you like apples?

They are good _____ you.

This _____ is red.

Write your own sentence using one or more of the sight words above. Remember to use a capital letter to begin your sentence. Use a punctuation mark to end your sentence.

_____

_____

_____

_____

Sight Words

Trace and write each word.

am

get

all

Circle the sight words in the puzzle below.
How many can you find?

g	n	a	l	l	a	g
e	g	a	o	a	l	e
t	c	e	m	m	l	t
a	m	s	t	p	n	o
a	l	l	h	l	a	m
g	e	t	u	a	l	l

Sight Words

am   get   All

Write the correct word to complete the sentence.

I _____ happy.

We _____ to play outside.

_____ my friends are here.

Write your own sentence using one or more of the sight words above. Remember to use a capital letter to begin your sentence. Use a punctuation mark to end your sentence.

_____

_____

_____

Sight Word Activities

SIGHT WORD FLASH CARDS

Sight words are words that a reader should recognize instantly. Most of these words are not decodable—you don't sound them out. Children who learn these words are well on their way to becoming successful readers. Carefully cut apart the 80 sight word flash cards found on pages 117-124.

Suggestions for using the Sight Word Flash Cards:

1. To begin, quickly show your child one card at a time and say the word. Learn a few words well, then move on to other words.

2. Turn the flash cards over one at a time. Show your child the card for two seconds. If your child can tell you the word before you turn the next card over, he gets to keep it; if not you keep the card. Whoever has the most cards at the end of the game is the winner.

3. Turn the flash cards over one at a time. Ask your child to identify the sight word and use the word in a simple sentence.

4. Place all the sight word flash cards in a bag or box. The object is to read as many sight words as possible in one minute. Set a timer for one minute. Ask your child to pull out a card and read it aloud. If he is correct he can keep the card; If he is incorrect, the card is set aside.

5. Lay one sight word flash card on the table. Help your child to write the word several times on a writing tablet or piece of paper.

6. Lay the sight word flash cards on the table. Say a sentence with a blank. Help your child select a sight word flash card that fillls in the blank to complete the sentence.

7. Play tic-tac-toe. Before placing an **x** or an **o** on the grid, your child must identify and/or spell a sight word correctly.

8. Look through magazines or newspapers, circle every "and," "the," or whatever word your child is learning!

TEACHERS:
Photocopy the flash cards and send them home with this activity page for additional practice.

a	all
am	and
are	at
big	can
can't	come

do	for
get	go
had	has
have	he
here	his

is	it
like	little
live	look
lots	me
my	on

one	said
see	she
that	the
there	they
this	to

up	want
was	we
went	what
where	who
why	will

with	you
fast	about
around	good
ask	did
down	help

one	two
three	four
five	six
seven	eight
nine	ten

red	orange
yellow	green
blue	purple
white	black
pink	gray

My Cat

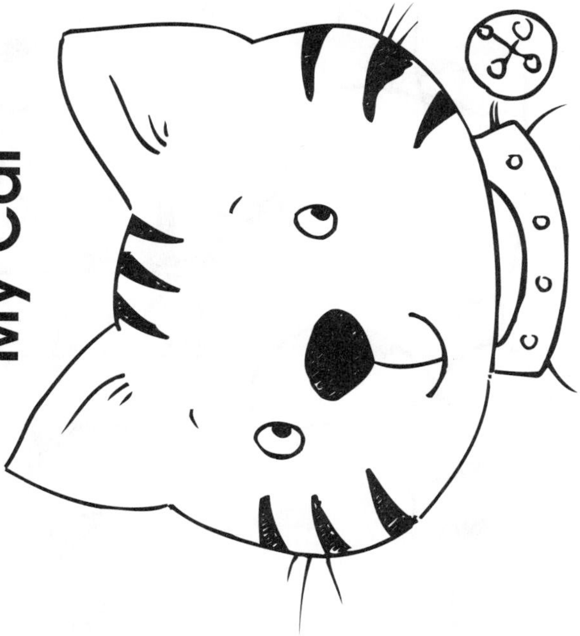

FOLD

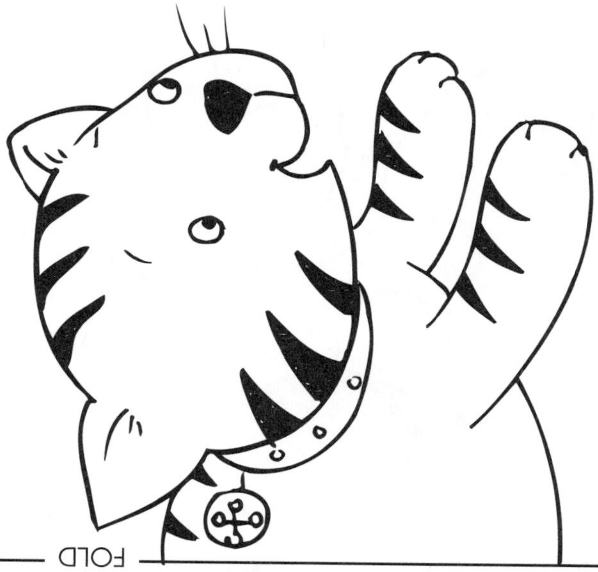

My cat can run.
3

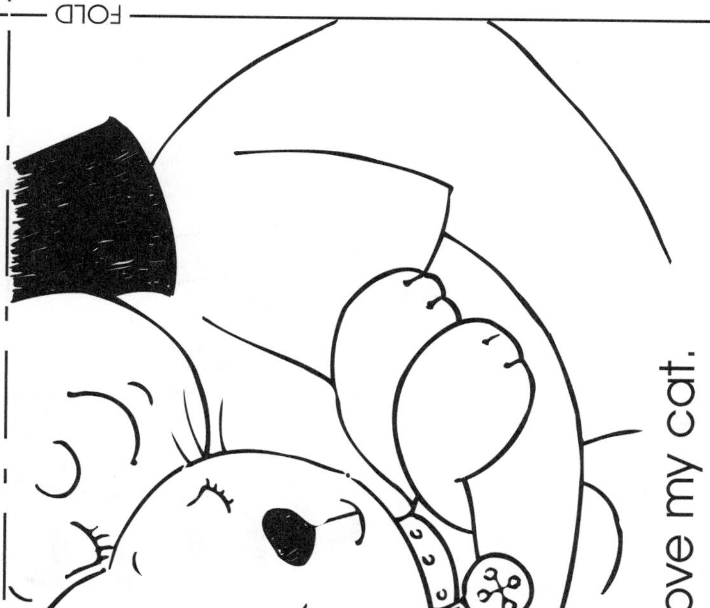

I love my cat.
8

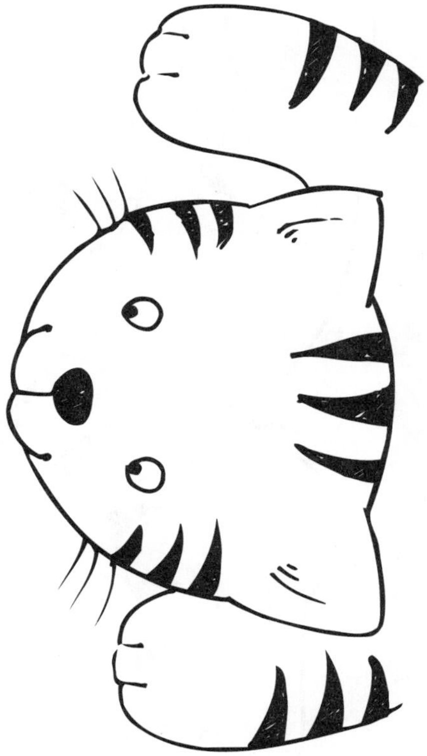

My cat can jump.
6

To assemble the Mini-Books:
1 Cut on dotted lines
2 Fold on solid lines
3 Put pages in correct order
4 Staple along left edge

My cat is big.
2

Run, cat, run!
4

Jump, cat, jump!
7

Stop, cat, stop!
5

FOLD

FOLD

Little or Big?

I am little.
3

© 2014 Twin Sisters IP, LLC. All Rights Reserved.

I am little. I am big.
8

Are you little?
6

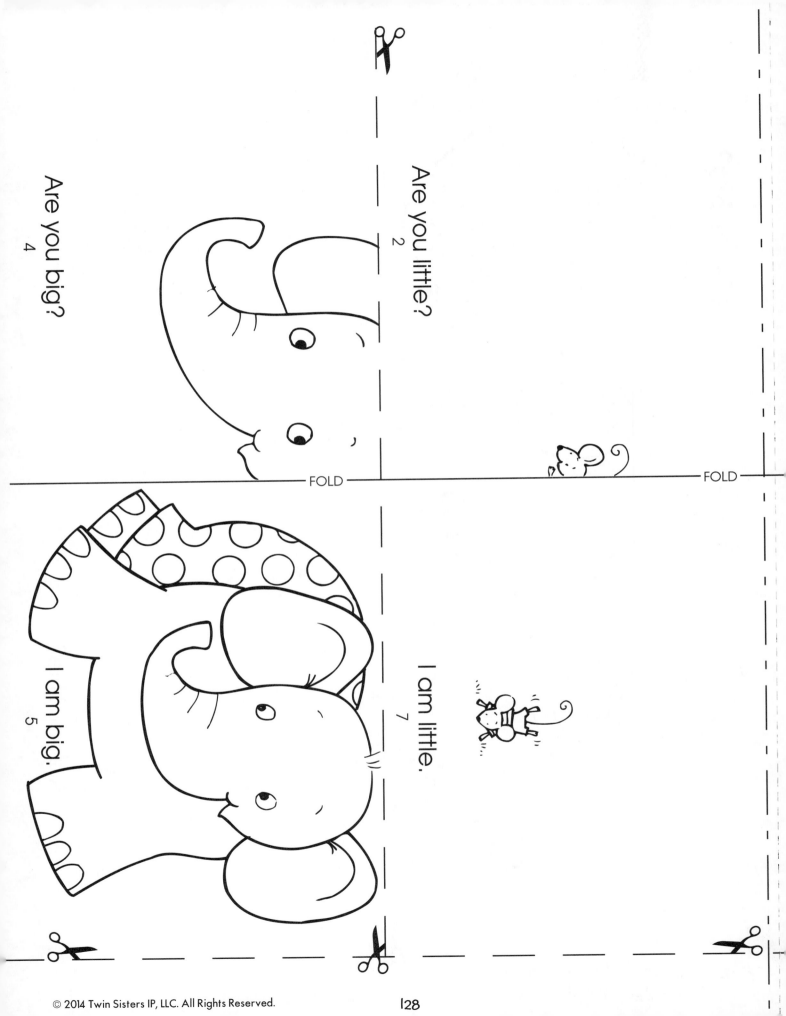

Are you little?
2

Are you big?
4

FOLD

FOLD

I am big.
5

I am little.
7

Up and Down

I can go down.
3

I can go up and down.
8

Yes, I can go up.
6

To assemble the Mini-Books: ① Cut on dotted lines ② Fold on solid lines ③ Put pages in correct order ④ Staple along left edge

129

I can go up.
2

Can you go up?
4

Yes, I can go down.
7

Can you go down?
5

My Friend

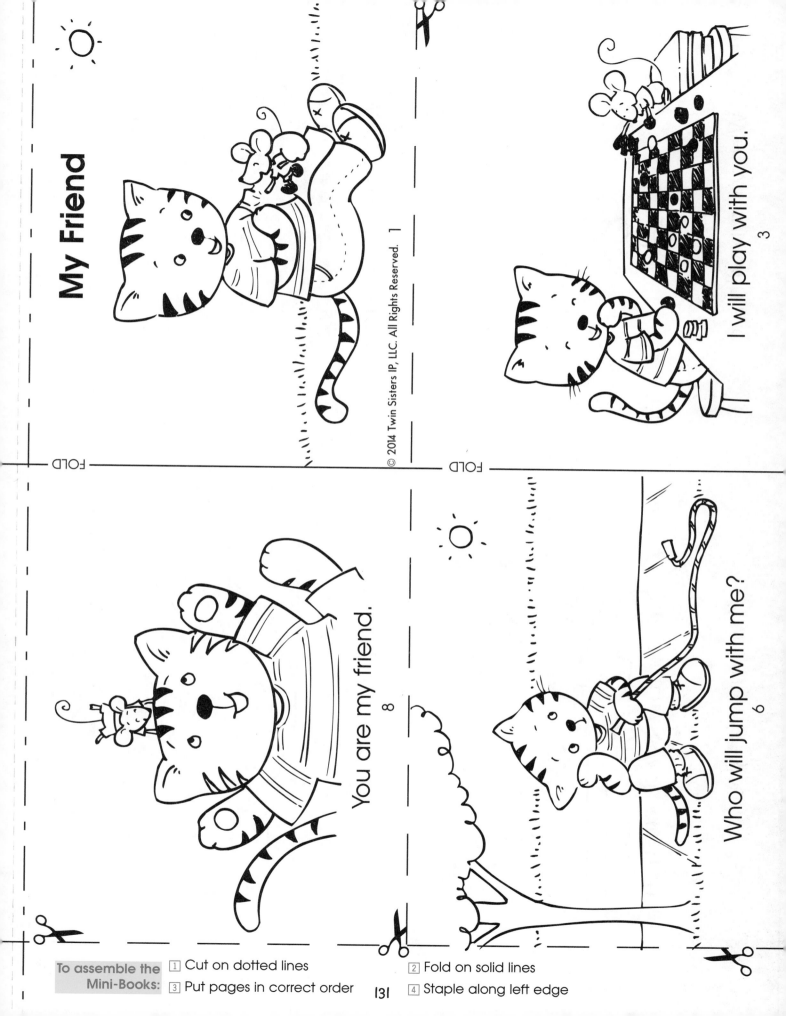

1

FOLD

I will play with you.

3

FOLD

You are my friend.

8

Who will jump with me?

6

To assemble the Mini-Books:
1. Cut on dotted lines
2. Fold on solid lines
3. Put pages in correct order
4. Staple along left edge

131

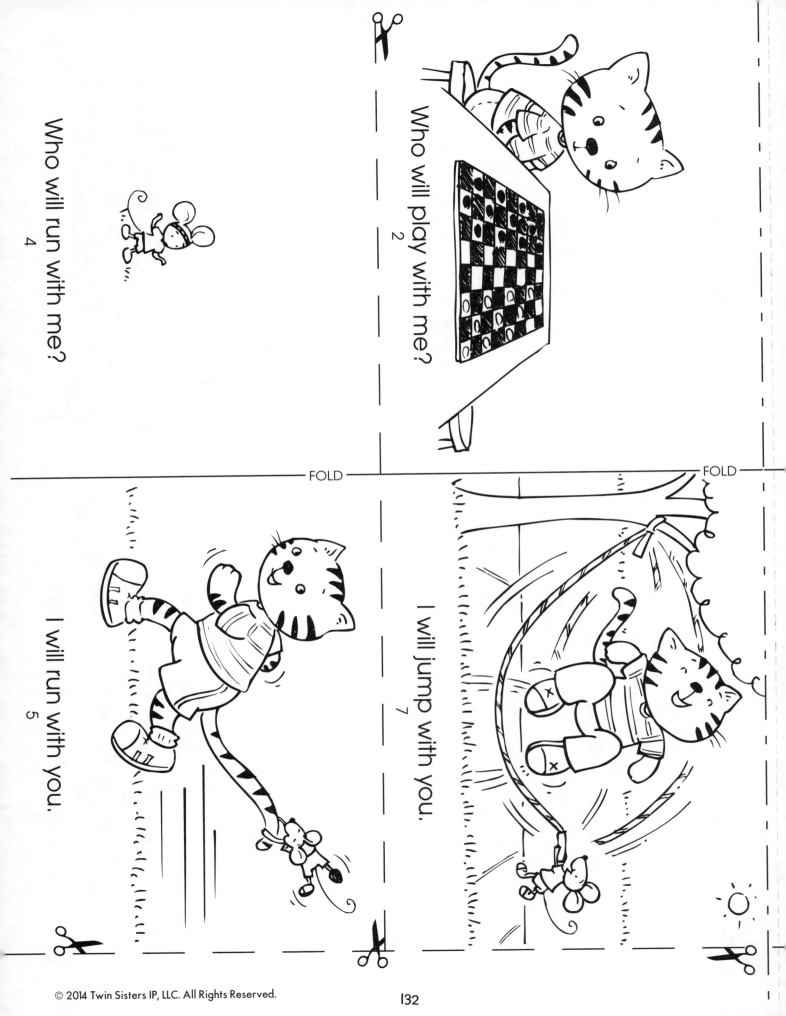

Who will play with me?
2

Who will run with me?
4

I will run with you.
5

I will jump with you.
7

Look!

Look at the little, green frog.

3

Look at the big, gray elephant.

6

Look at them all.

8

FOLD

FOLD

To assemble the Mini-Books:
1 Cut on dotted lines
3 Put pages in correct order
2 Fold on solid lines
4 Staple along left edge

133

Look at the little, blue bird.
2

Look at the little, red bug.
4

Look at the big, brown bear.
5

Look at the big, pink pig.
7

FOLD

FOLD

Help! Where Is My Home?

This is my home.

8

Help! Where is my home?
Is this my home?

6

Help! Where is my home?
Is this my home?

3

1

FOLD

FOLD

FOLD

To assemble the Mini-Books:

1 Cut on dotted lines

2 Fold on solid lines

3 Put pages in correct order

4 Staple along left edge

Help! Where is my home?
Is this my home?
4

Help! Where is my home?
Is this my home?
2

FOLD

FOLD

Help! Where is my home?
Is this my home?
5

Help! Where is my home?
Is this my home?
7

May I Read a Book to You?

1

FOLD

3

May I go down the slide with you?
You may go down the slide with me.

FOLD

May I read a book to you?
You may read a book to me.
8

May I show you how to skip?
You may show me how to skip.
6

To assemble the Mini-Books:

1 Cut on dotted lines

2 Fold on solid lines

3 Put pages in correct order

4 Staple along left edge

137

May I come in your house?
You may come in my house.

2

May I eat cake with you?
You may eat cake with me.

4

May I go to school with you?
You may go to school with me.

7

May I help you clean up?
You may help me clean up.

5

Questions

© 2014 Twin Sisters IP, LLC. All Rights Reserved.   1

FOLD

What are you eating?
I am eating an apple.
3

FOLD

FOLD

Thank you.
8

Will you clean up your mess?
Yes, I will clean up my mess.
6

Where are you going?
I am going outside.
2

When will you be home?
I will be home soon.
4

FOLD

FOLD

Do you want a cookie?
Yes, I want a cookie.
7

Why are you running?
I am playing a game.
5

Rhyming Word Fun

FROG LOG

BIG PIG

HEN PEN

DOG JOG

CAT

BUG RUG

FOLD

Look at the pig.
She is big.
Look at the pig dancing a jig.

3

FOLD

Look at the cat.
Look at the pig.
Look at the hen in her pen.
Look at the bug.
Look at the dog.
Look at the frog on the log.

8

Look at the hen.
She is in her pen.
Look at the hen in her pen.

6

To assemble the Mini-Books:

1. Cut on dotted lines
2. Fold on solid lines
3. Put pages in correct order
4. Staple along left edge

141

Look at the cat.
He is fat.
Look at the cat with the funny hat.

2

Look at the frog.
He jumped to the log.
Look at the frog on the log.

4

Look at the dog.
He likes to jog.
Look at the dog named Zog.

7

Look at the bug.
She is on the rug.
Look at the bug with a mug.

5

FOLD

FOLD

Five Little Fish

5

Four little fish swam in a stream.
Red and blue and one was green.
They swam around until one said,
"I am tired. I'm going to bed."

3

FOLD

Five little fish swam in a stream.
Red and blue and one was green.
They swam around then they all said,
"We're not tired. Let's play instead."

8

One little fish swam in a stream.
He was not red or blue, but green.
He swam around until he said,
"I am tired. I'm going to bed."

9

To assemble the Mini-Books:
1. Cut on dotted lines
2. Fold on solid lines
3. Put pages in correct order
4. Staple along left edge

Five little fish swam in a stream.
Red and blue and one was green.
They swam around until one said,
"I am tired. I'm going to bed."

2

Three little fish swam in a stream.
Red and blue and one was green.
They swam around until one said,
"I am tired. I'm going to bed."

4

So tired and sad he stopped right then.
He found his friends asleep in bed.
He snuggled down, fell asleep just when
All his friends began to play again!

7

Two little fish swam in a stream.
Red and blue and one was green.
They swam around until one said,
"I am tired. I'm going to bed."

5

FOLD

FOLD

Fun With Seven

7 seven

Trace then write the number 7.

7

Trace then write the number word **seven**.

seven

Circle **seven** turtles.

Fun With Eight

8 eight

Trace then write the number **8**.

8

Trace then write the number word **eight**.

eight

Circle **eight** birds.

9 nine

Trace then write the number 9.

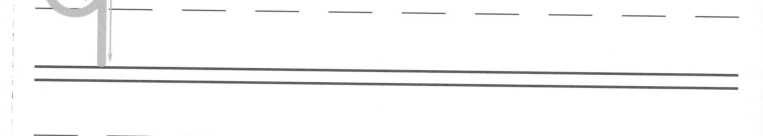

Trace then write the number word **nine**.

Circle **nine** stars.

Fun With Ten

10 ten

Trace then write the number 10.

10

Trace then write the number word ten.

ten

Circle ten bears.

Fun With Eleven

11 eleven

Trace then write the number 11.

Trace then write the number word **eleven**.

Circle **eleven** apples.

Fun With Twelve

12 twelve

Trace then write the number 12.

12

Trace then write the number word twelve.

twelve

Circle twelve elephants.

13 thirteen

Trace then write the number 13.

13

Trace then write the number word thirteen.

thirteen

Circle thirteen mice.

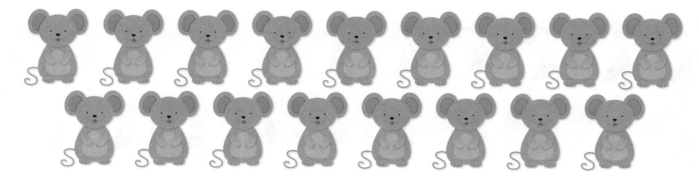

Fun With Fourteen

14 fourteen

Trace then write the number 14.

14

Trace then write the number word **fourteen**.

fourteen

Circle **fourteen** balls.

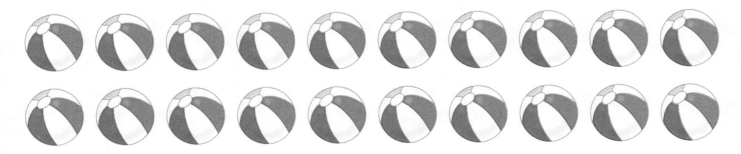

15 fifteen

Trace then write the number 15.

15

Trace then write the number word fifteen.

fifteen

Circle fifteen butterflies.

16 sixteen

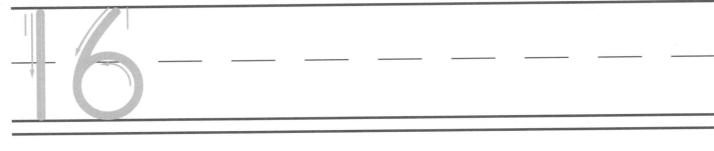

Trace then write the number 16.

16

Trace then write the number word sixteen.

sixteen

Circle sixteen penguins.

17 seventeen

Trace then write the number **17**.

Trace then write the number word **seventeen**.

seventeen

Circle **seventeen** ladybugs.

Fun With Eighteen

18 eighteen

Trace then write the number 18.

18

Trace then write the number word eighteen.

eighteen

Circle eighteen ducks.

19 nineteen

Trace then write the number 19.

Trace then write the number word **nineteen**.

nineteen

Circle **nineteen** suns.

20 twenty

Trace then write the number **20**.

20

Trace then write the number word **twenty**.

twenty

Circle **twenty** fish.

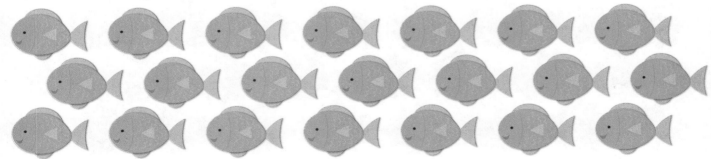

Counting Activities

Count how many in each group. Circle the correct number.

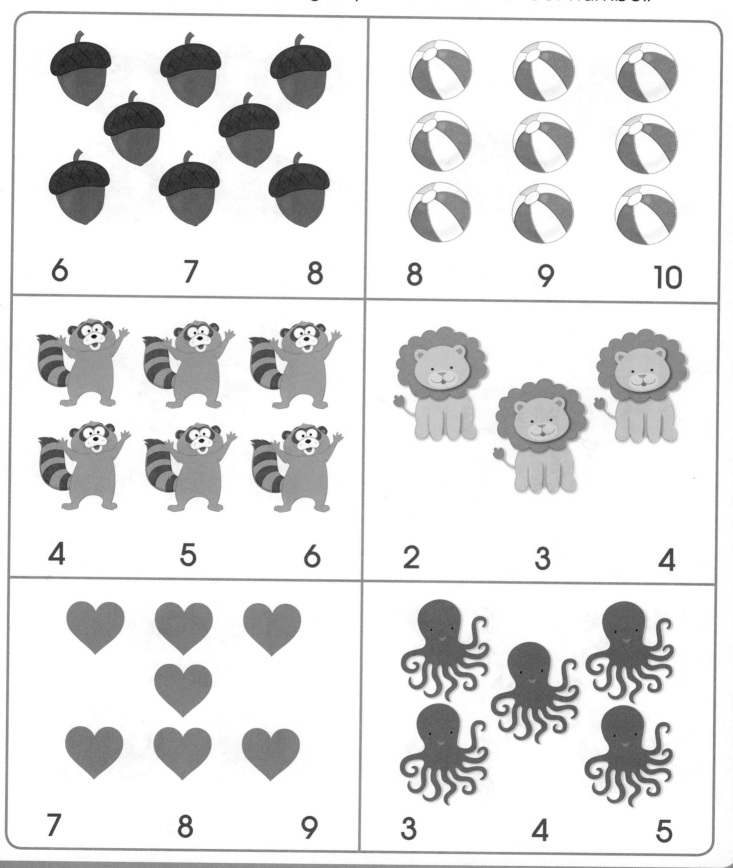

6   7   8

8   9   10

4   5   6

2   3   4

7   8   9

3   4   5

Counting Activities

Count how many in each group. Circle the correct number.

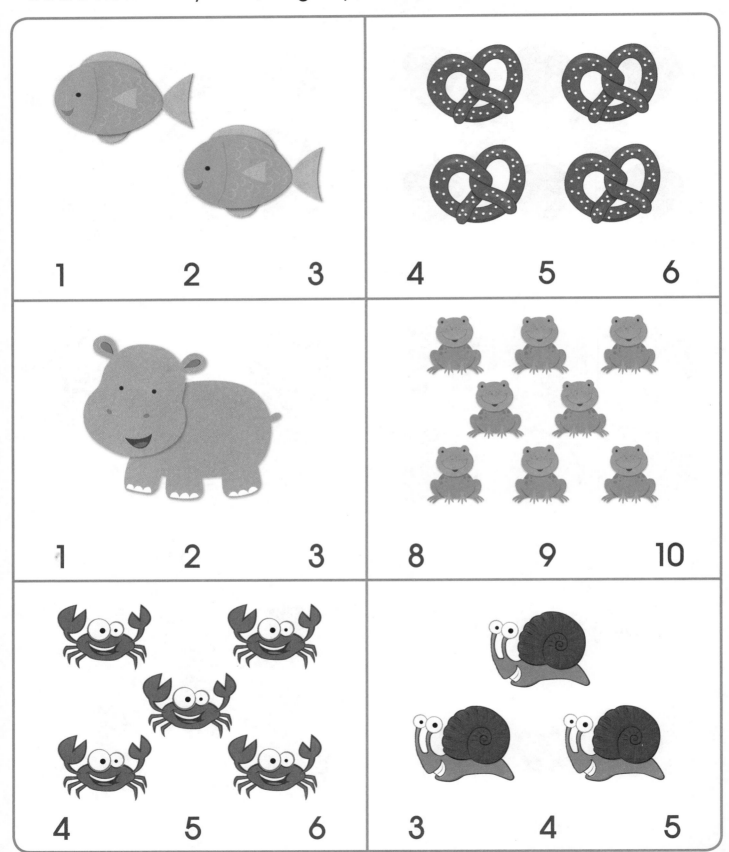

1   2   3

4   5   6

1   2   3

8   9   10

4   5   6

3   4   5

Counting Activities

Count how many in each group. Circle the correct number.

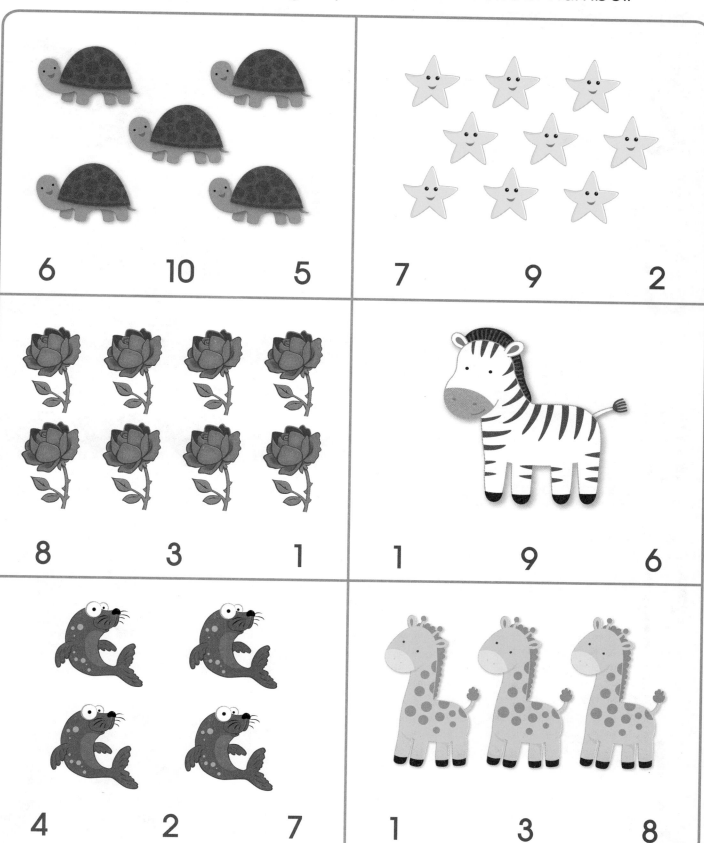

6   10   5

7   9   2

8   3   1

1   9   6

4   2   7

1   3   8

Counting 1-5

Count. Draw lines to match the number to the correct number of objects.

2

3

5

4

1

Count. Draw lines to match the number to the correct number of objects.

6

9

7

8

10

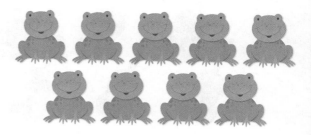

Counting Fun

Count. Write how many.

_6_

___ ___

___ ___

___ ___

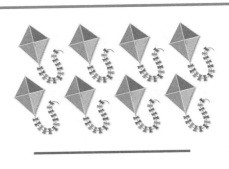

___ ___

___ ___ ___

___ ___

Matching Fun

Count. Draw lines to match the number to the correct number of objects.

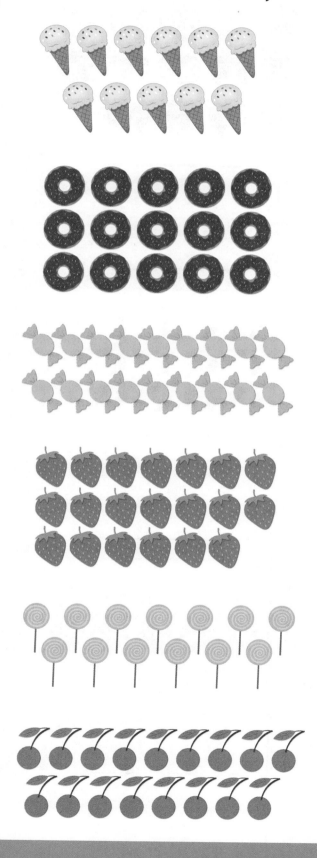

20

13

11

17

18

15

Counting Fun

Count. Write how many.

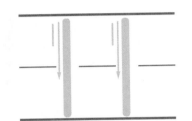

_ _ _

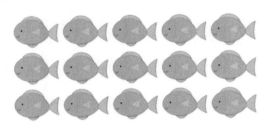

_ _ _

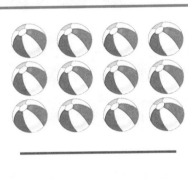

_ _ _

_ _ _

_ _ _

Counting Fun

Count. Write how many.

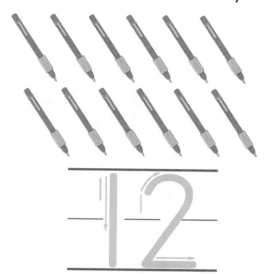

12

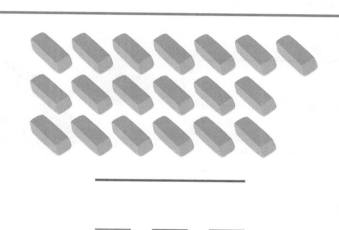

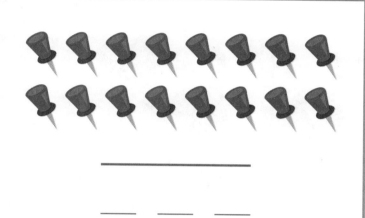

Counting Fun

Count each group. Write how many there are in each row.

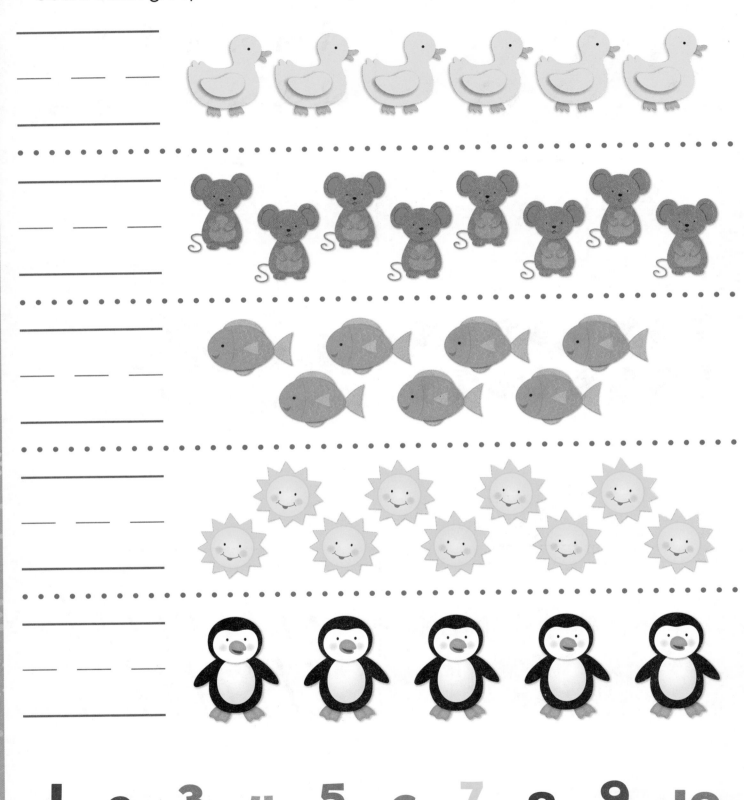

1 2 3 4 5 6 7 8 9 10

Counting Fun

Count each group. Write how many there are in each row.

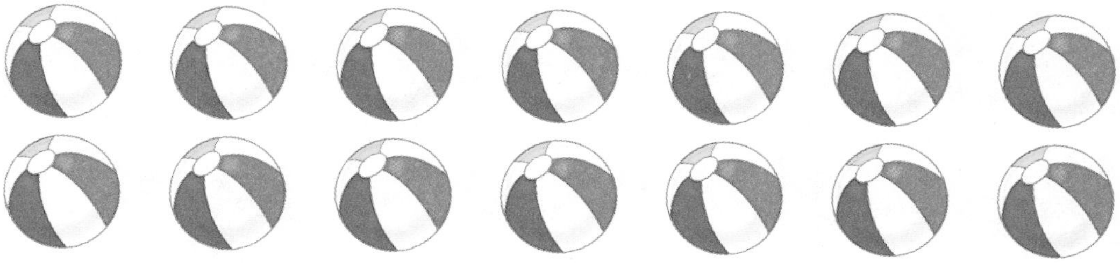

_____

___ ___ ___

_____

___ ___ ___

_____

___ ___ ___

_____

___ ___ ___

_____

___ ___ ___

11 12 13 14 15 16 17 18 19 20

Counting 1-5 Review

Say each number. Point to each picture and count out loud.
Trace the number word.

1 — one

2 — two

3 — three

4 — four

5 — five

Counting 6-10 Review

Say each number. Point to each picture and count out loud. Trace the number word.

6 six

7 seven

8 eight

9 nine

10 ten

Number Words

Match each number to the correct number word.

1	five
2	three
3	one
4	four
5	two

Number Words

Match each number to the correct number word.

6

7

8

9

10

nine

ten

six

eight

seven

Before

3 comes **before** 4.
Write the number that comes before.

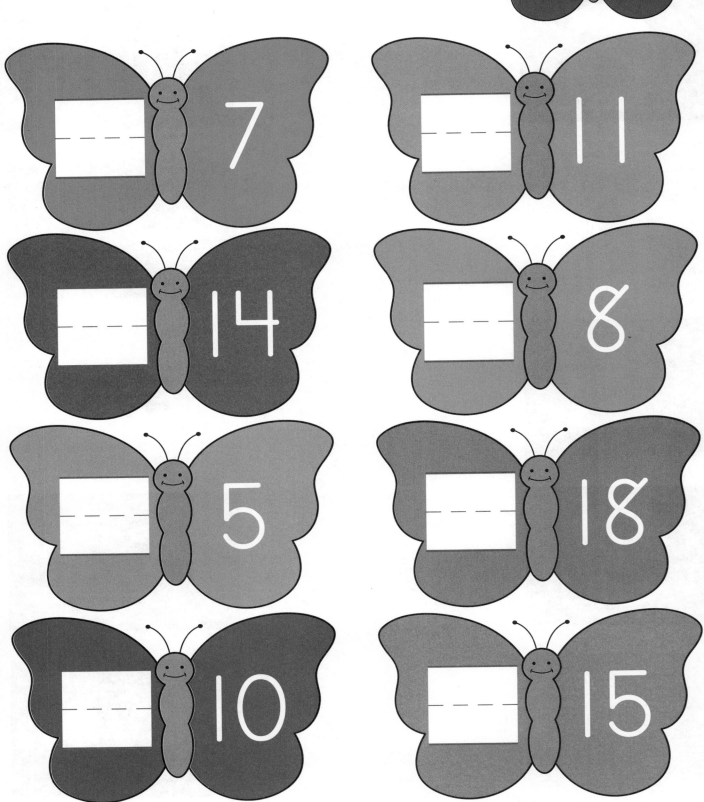

After

6 comes **after** 5.
Write the number that comes after.

Numbers From 1-10

Count the things in each group.
Then trace each number to show how many.

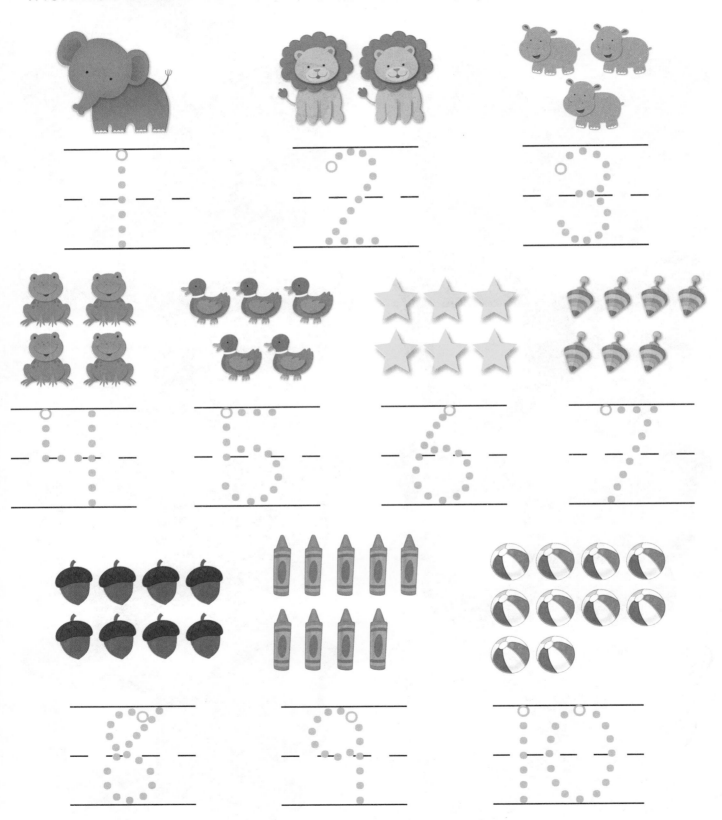

Numbers From 11-20

Count the things in each group.
Then trace each number to show how many.

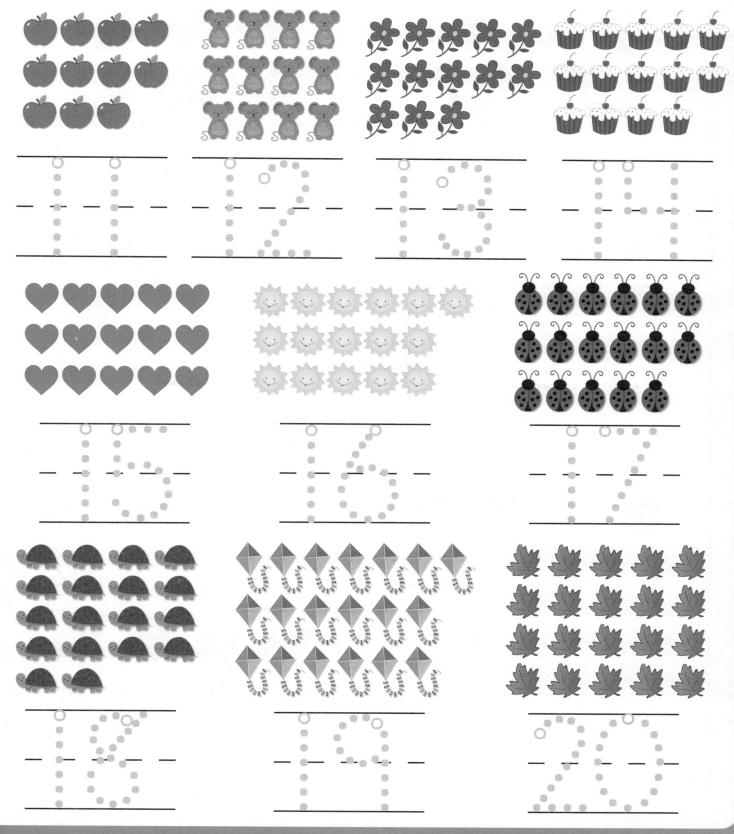

Counting Activities

Write the number that comes between the given numbers.

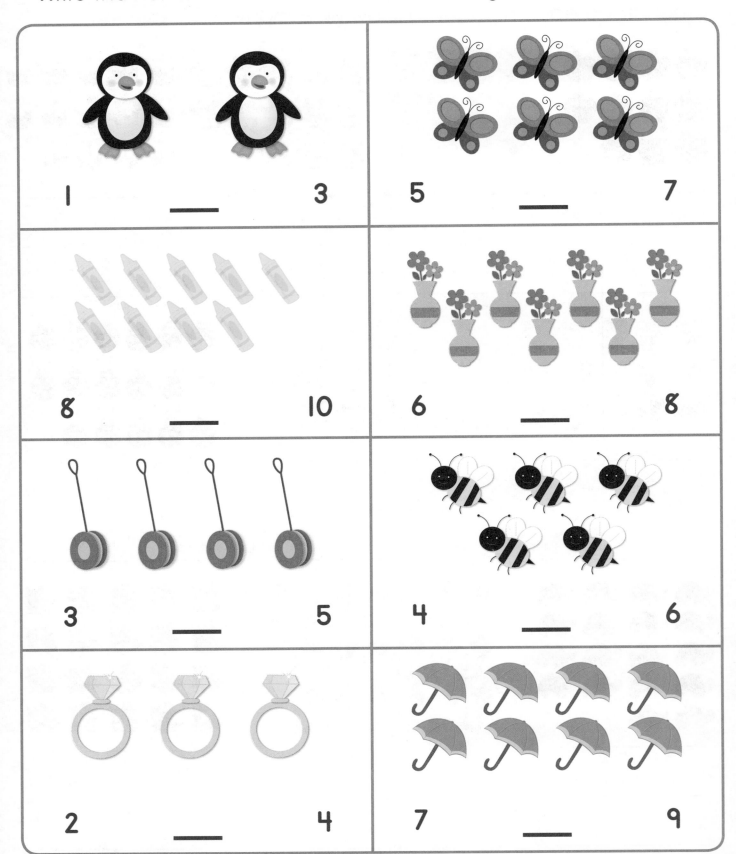

1 ___ 3

5 ___ 7

8 ___ 10

6 ___ 8

3 ___ 5

4 ___ 6

2 ___ 4

7 ___ 9

Missing Numbers

Write the missing numbers.

1 ___ 3 ___ 5

8 ___ 10 11 ___

___ 16 ___ 18 19

6 7 ___ 9 ___

Missing Numbers

Write the missing numbers.

5 ___ 7 8 9 ___

___ 2 3 ___ 5

10 11 ___ 13 ___

16 ___ 18 ___ 20

If I Had $100

HOORAY! Let's celebrate **100 days of school**. If you had $100, what would you buy? Who would you help if you had $100? If you had $100, where would you like to visit? Make a list and share it with your friends.

If I had $100...

_____

_____

_____

_____

_____

_____

_____

_____

_____

_____

_____

_____

_____

Skip Counting To 100

Count to 100 by skip counting by **tens**.

10									

Count to 100 by skip counting by **fives**.

5					

Count to 100 by skip counting by **twos**.

2					

If you found 100 pieces of bubble gum what would you do?

_____

- -

_____

_____

I Can Write To 100

Fill in the missing numbers.

1									
				15					
21									30
			34						
	42								
								59	
		63							
							78		
				85					
91									100

Learning Addition & Subtraction

Addition

A fun way for children to learn the concept of addition is to use concrete objects. Try using cereal, pennies, crayons, or small toys. For example, place 3 toy cars in one group and place 2 toy cars in another group. Have your child or student count aloud each group. Then have him or her put the groups together and count again. Demonstrate each step by saying 3 cars plus 2 cars equals 5 cars.

Teach that when learning addition facts, the numbers to be added together are called addends. The answer is called the sum. You can change the order of the addends around, but the sum will remain the same. For example: 3+2=5, and 2+3=5. Again, demonstrate this concept using concrete objects. The goal is for children to understand the concept of addition, not remember initially all of the terms. Keep the teaching time very short, positive, and fun. Be encouraging and focus on little successes.

Addition Words

Addends: The numbers that are added.

Addition: To combine ADDENDS into one SUM.

Sum: The answer in addition.

Plus Sign: + The symbol in a number sentence that tells you that you are supposed to add. When you see 2+3 you say, "Two plus three."

Equal Sign: = The symbol in a number sentence that tells you that the numbers on either side have the same value. In 2+3=5, the number 5 has the same value as 2+3.

$$\begin{array}{r} 3 \\ + 4 \\ \hline 7 \end{array}$$

addends

sum

Subtraction

When teaching the concept of subtraction use concrete objects as well. For example, place 5 crayons in a row. Take 2 crayons away. Say, "There were 5 crayons and I took 2 crayons away. How many crayons are left?" Then state the subtraction problem is 5-2=3

Subtraction Words

Subtraction: An operation that takes some away from another.

Difference: The answer in subtraction.

Minus Sign: - The symbol in a number sentence that tells you that you are supposed to subtract. When you read 3-2 you say, "Three minus two."

5 - 2 = 3

Simple Addition

Count. Write how many in all.

 +    **in all**
_____

     **in all**
_____

 +     **in all**
_____

 +   **in all**
_____

 +  **in all**
_____

191

Simple Addition

Count. Write how many in all.

 +    **in all**

_____

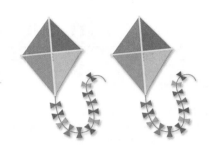 +    **in all**

_____

 +    **in all**

_____

 +   **in all**

_____

+    **in all**

_____

Adding Fun

Count. Write how many in all.

1 + 2 = 3

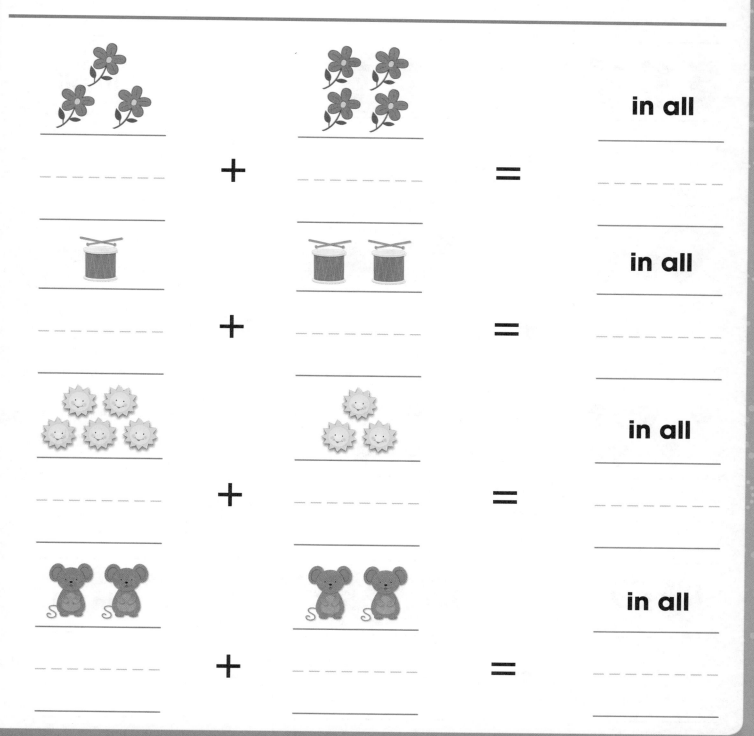

____ + ____ = ____ in all

____ + ____ = ____ in all

____ + ____ = ____ in all

____ + ____ = ____ in all

Adding Fun

Count. Write how many in all.

+   =   in all

+   =   in all

+   =   in all

+   =   in all

+   =   in all

Addition

Count. Write how many in all.

```
  _____

  _ _ _ _ _ _

+ _ _ _ _ _ _
  _____

  _ _ _ _ _ _

  _____
```

in all

```
  _____

  _ _ _ _ _ _

+ _____

  _____

  _ _ _ _ _ _

  _____
```

in all

```
  _____

  _ _ _ _ _ _

+ _ _ _ _ _ _
  _____

  _ _ _ _ _ _

  _____
```

in all

```
  _____

  _ _ _ _ _ _

+ _____

  _____

  _ _ _ _ _ _

  _____
```

in all

Addition

Count. Write how many in all.

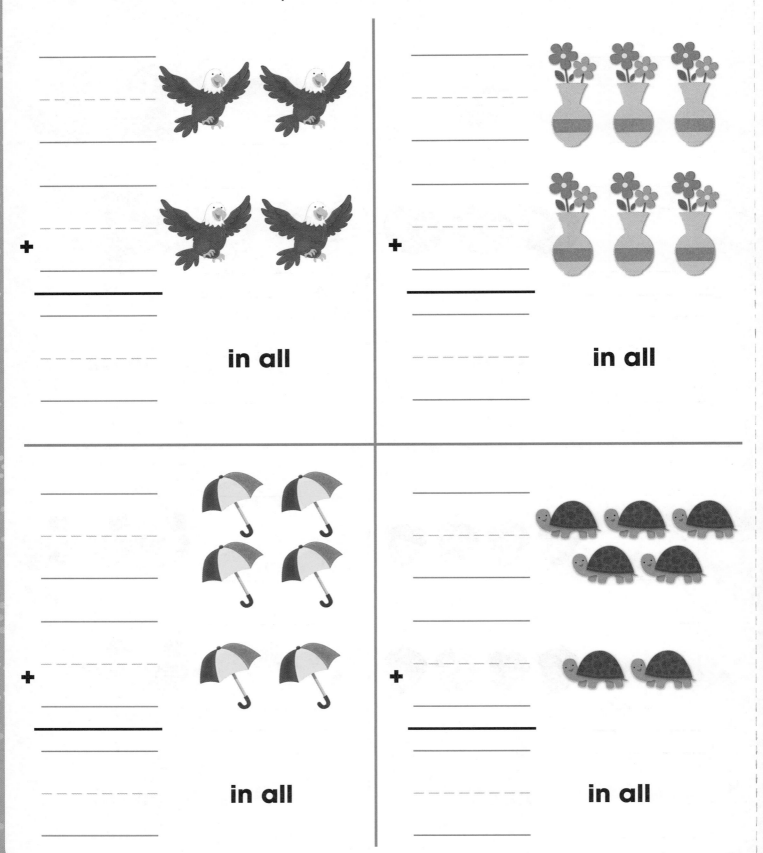

in all

in all

in all

in all

Addition

Count. Write how many in all.

_____
- - - - - - - - -
_____
_____
+
_____
═════════════════
_____
- - - - - - - - -
in all
_____

_____
- - - - - - - - -
_____
_____
+
_____
═════════════════
_____
- - - - - - - - -
in all
_____

_____
- - - - - - - - -
_____
_____
+
_____
═════════════════
_____
- - - - - - - - -
in all
_____

_____
- - - - - - - - -
_____
_____
+
_____
═════════════════
_____
- - - - - - - - -
in all
_____

Adding Sums To 10

Add to find each sum. Write the answers.

$3 + 7 =$ 10

$6 + 2 =$ _____

$4 + 5 =$ _____

$5 + 5 =$ _____

3
+4 _____

8
+1 _____

4
+6 _____

Domino Addition

Add. Write each sum.

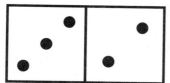

3 + 2 = _____ 5

3
+ 2
_____
5
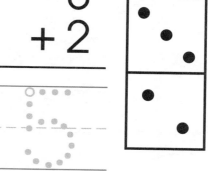

2 + 4 = _____

3 + 4 = _____

5
+ 3
_____
_____
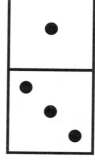

1
+ 3
_____
_____

2
+ 7
_____
_____
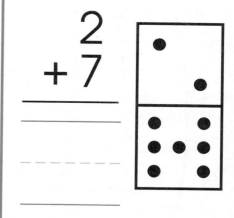

2
+ 2
_____
_____

4
+ 6
_____
_____

5
+ 5
_____
_____
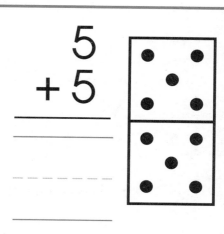

Coloring Fun

Add. Color the picture using the code.

5 =
6 =
7 =
8 =
9 =
10 =

6+0=

3+3=

5+1=

$\dfrac{5}{+3}$

$\dfrac{6}{+4}$

$\dfrac{2}{+5}$

$\dfrac{5}{+4}$

$\dfrac{4}{+1}$

4+2=

5+5=

6+0=

6+2=

$\dfrac{2}{+3}$

4+4=

8+2=

7+1=

Batter Up Addition

Add. Write each sum.

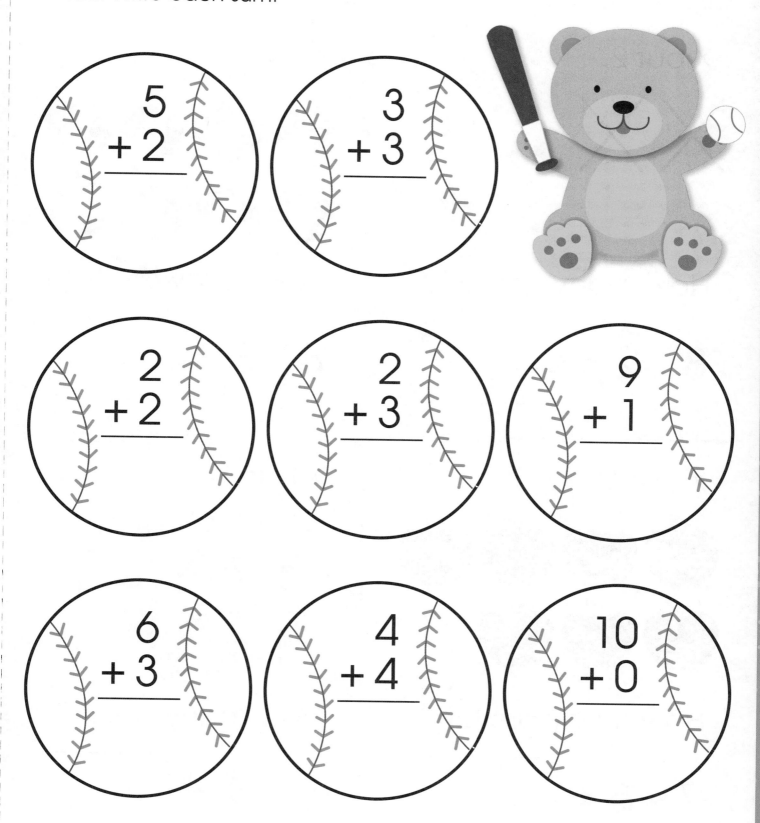

$$\begin{array}{r} 5 \\ +2 \\ \hline \end{array}$$

$$\begin{array}{r} 3 \\ +3 \\ \hline \end{array}$$

$$\begin{array}{r} 2 \\ +2 \\ \hline \end{array}$$

$$\begin{array}{r} 2 \\ +3 \\ \hline \end{array}$$

$$\begin{array}{r} 9 \\ +1 \\ \hline \end{array}$$

$$\begin{array}{r} 6 \\ +3 \\ \hline \end{array}$$

$$\begin{array}{r} 4 \\ +4 \\ \hline \end{array}$$

$$\begin{array}{r} 10 \\ +0 \\ \hline \end{array}$$

Simple Subtraction

Cross out and subtract. Write the answer.

X out 2.

How many are left?

8 - 2 = 6

X out 3.

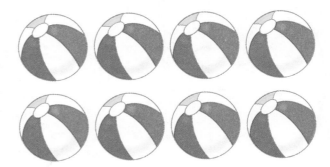

How many are left?

8 - 3 =

X out 6.

How many are left?

7 - 6 =

X out 4.

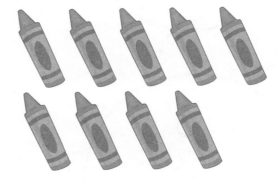

How many are left?

9 - 4 =

Simple Subtraction

Cross out and subtract. Write the answer.

X out 1.

How many are left?

4 - 1 = _____

X out 3.

How many are left?

6 - 3 = _____

X out 4.

How many are left?

8 - 4 = _____

X out 2.

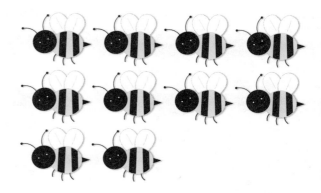

How many are left?

10 - 2 = _____

Subtract

Cross out and subtract. Write the answer.

$$6$$
$$-\ 4$$
$$2$$

$$4$$
$$-\ 1$$

How many are left? _____

$$5$$
$$-\ 3$$

How many are left? _____

$$6$$
$$-\ 2$$

How many are left? _____

$$7$$
$$-\ 1$$

How many are left? _____

Subtract

Cross out and subtract. Write the answer.

$$8 - 5$$

How many are left? _____

$$3 - 2$$

How many are left? _____

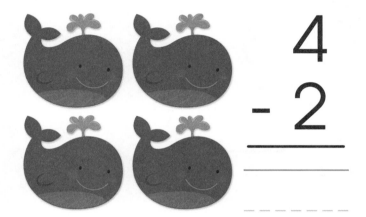
$$4 - 2$$

How many are left? _____

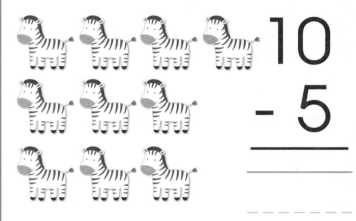
$$10 - 5$$

How many are left? _____

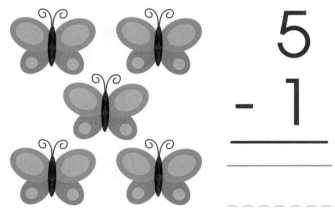
$$5 - 1$$

How many are left? _____

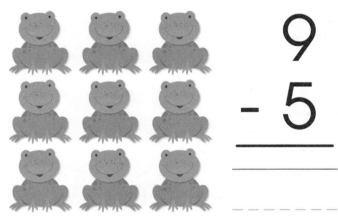
$$9 - 5$$

How many are left? _____

Subtracting

Subtracting shows how many are left. Draw shapes to help you subtract.

$$\begin{array}{r} 6 \\ -\ 3 \\ \hline \end{array}$$

$$\begin{array}{r} 8 \\ -\ 2 \\ \hline \end{array}$$

$$\begin{array}{r} 5 \\ -\ 4 \\ \hline \end{array}$$

$$\begin{array}{r} 3 \\ -\ 1 \\ \hline \end{array}$$

$$\begin{array}{r} 7 \\ -\ 3 \\ \hline \end{array}$$

$$\begin{array}{r} 9 \\ -\ 4 \\ \hline \end{array}$$

What Is A Circle?

This is a circle. Trace the circles.

A circle has no sides. It is round like a ball.

Circle the objects that are circles.

What Is A Square?

This is a square. Trace the squares.

A square has four sides. Each side is the same.

Circle the objects that are squares.

What Is A Triangle?

This is a triangle. Trace the triangle.

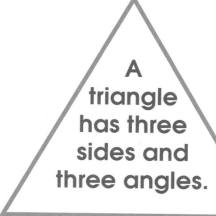

A triangle has three sides and three angles.

Circle the objects that are triangles.

What Is A Rectangle?

This is a rectangle. Trace the rectangles.

A rectangle has two long sides, two short sides, and four angles.

Circle the objects that are rectangles.

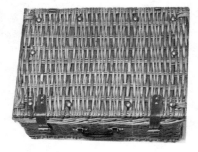

What Is An Oval?

This is an oval. Trace the oval.

An oval looks like an egg. It has no sides.

Circle the objects that are ovals.

What Is A Rhombus?

This is a rhombus. Trace the rhombuses.

A rhombus is shaped like a diamond and has four sides that are all the same length. A rhombus also has four angles.

Circle the objects that are rhombuses.

What Is A Hexagon?

This is a hexagon. Trace the hexagon.

A hexagon has six sides and six angles.

Circle the hexagons.

What Is An Octagon?

This is an octagon. Trace the octagons.

An octagon has eight sides and eight angles.

Circle the octagons.

Match The Shapes

Draw a line to match the shapes that are the same.

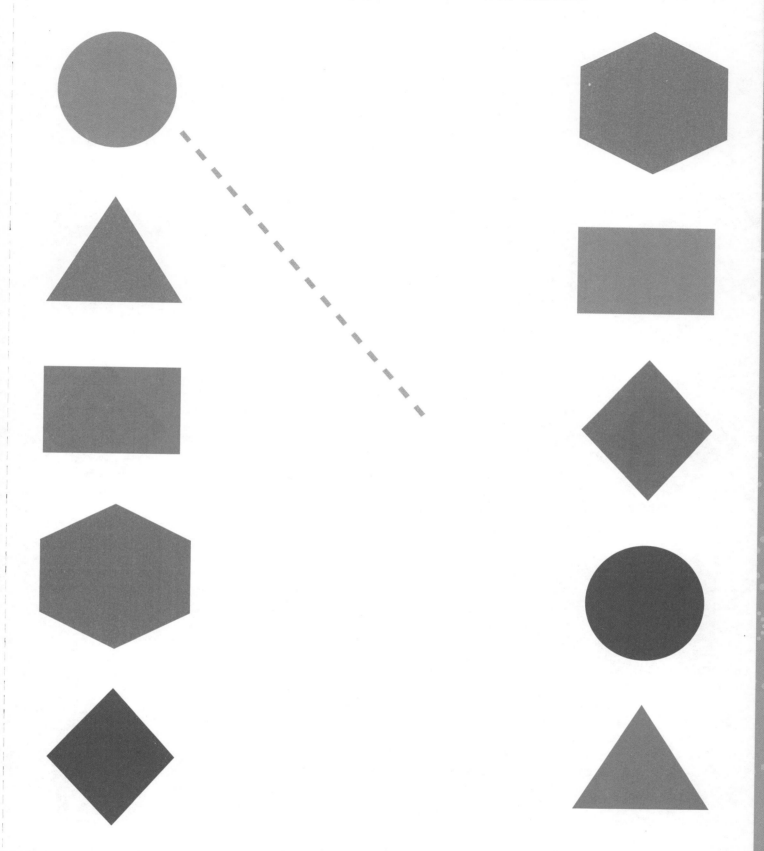

Match The Shapes

Draw a line to match the shapes that are the same.

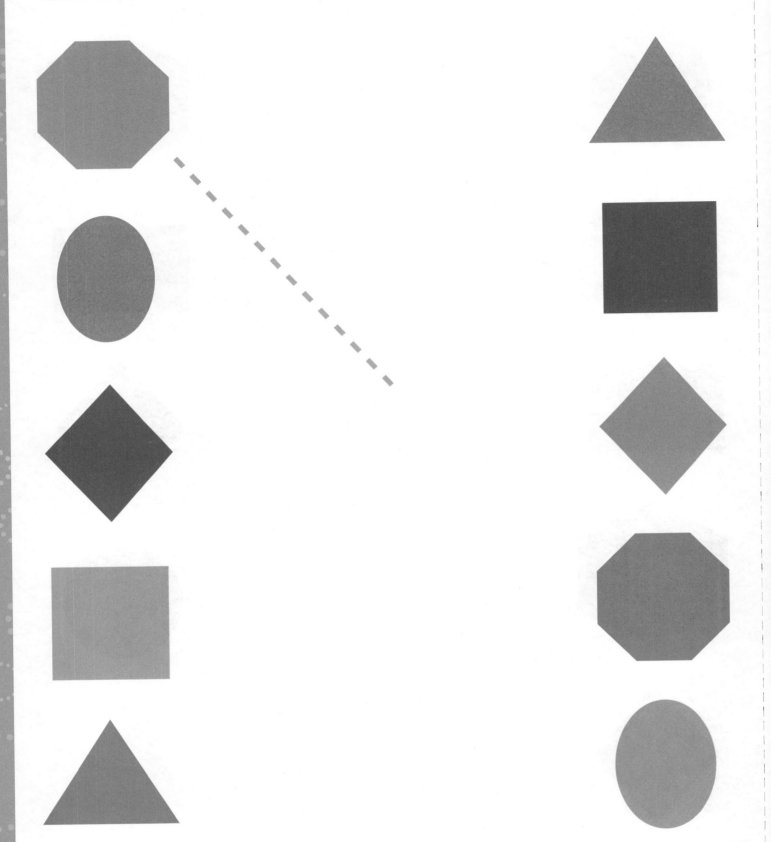

Shapes In The World

Match the shape to the object that has the same shape.

Shape Patterns

Draw and color the shape that comes next.

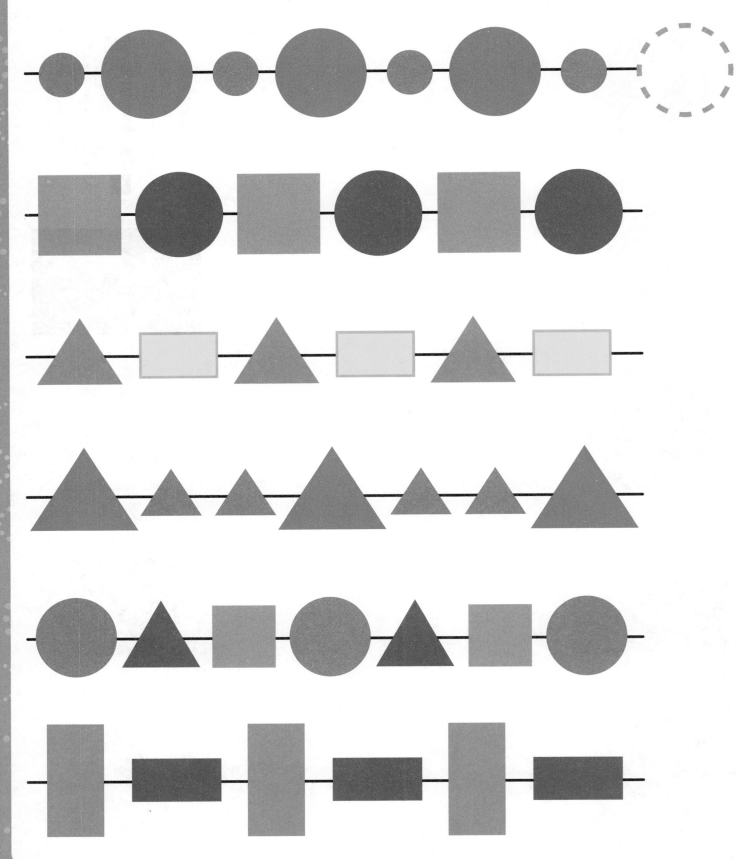

Same Shape

Circle the shape that is the same.

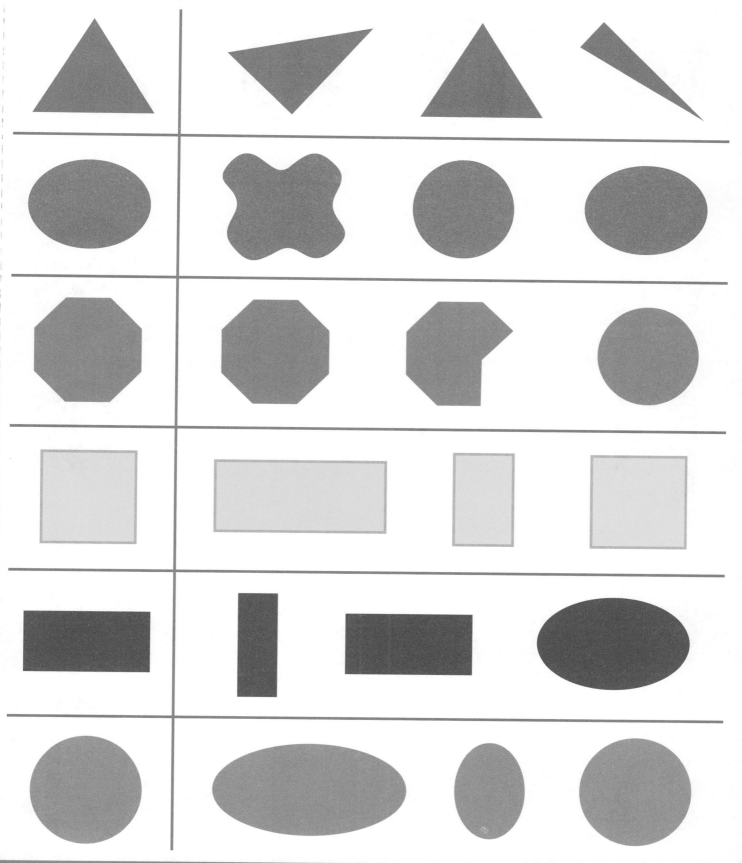

Finding Shapes

Match each shape to the object that has the same shape.

cube   cylinder   sphere   cone

The Color Red

The wagon is **red**.

Trace then write the color **red**.

red

Circle things that are **red**.

The Color Blue

The fish is **blue**.

Trace then write the color **blue**.

blue

Circle things that are **blue**.

The Color Yellow

The banana is yellow.

Trace then write the color yellow.

yellow

Circle things that are yellow.

The Color Green

The frog is **green**.

Trace then write the color **green**.

green

Circle things that are **green**.

The Color Orange

The pumpkin is orange.

Trace then write the color orange.

Circle things that are orange.

225

The Color Purple

The balloon is **purple**.

Trace then write the color **purple**.

purple

Circle things that are **purple**.

The Color Brown

The dog is **brown**.

Trace then write the color **brown**.

brown

Circle things that are **brown**.

The Color Black

The horse is **black**.

Trace then write the color **black**.

black

Circle things that are **black**.

The Color White

The egg is white.

Trace then write the color white.

white

Circle things that are white.

The Color Gray

The elephant is gray.

Trace then write the color **gray**.

gray₂

Circle things that are **gray**.

The flower is **pink**.

Trace then write the color pink.

pink

Circle things that are pink.

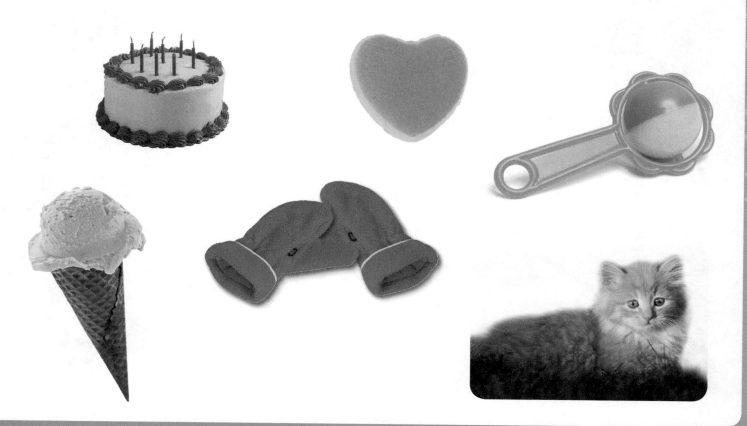

Rhyming Words

Draw lines to match the pictures that rhyme.

Rhyming Words

Draw lines to match the pictures that rhyme.

Create A Rhyming Book

Download **A Little Cat, Cat, Cat** and then use the song to emphasize that the beginning letter is the only change to create many rhyming words. Then photocopy the pages and have each child create their own rhyming book. Simply have them fill in the rhyming word on the template provided and illustrate their story. Finally, cut on the dotted lines and staple the book together.

A Little Cat, Cat, Cat

A little cat, cat, cat
Sat on a mat, mat, mat
And wore a hat, hat, hat
And liked to chat, chat, chat
And the little cat, cat, cat
Was mighty fat, fat, fat
What do you think of that?

There was a dog, dog, dog
Who liked a frog, frog, frog
Down by the bog, bog, bog
Up on a log, log, log
Now that dog, dog, dog
Would often jog, jog, jog
To see his friend the frog.

Miss Pretty Pig, Pig, Pig
Wore a wig, wig, wig
While doing the jig, jig, jig
Eating a fig, fig, fig
Now Pretty Pig, Pig, Pig
Said it's her gig, gig, gig
Can you really dig?

Now little cat, cat, cat
On the mat, mat, mat
And the dog, dog, dog
That liked the frog, frog, frog
And Miss Pig, Pig, Pig
Who wore a wig, wig, wig
It's a rhyming thing-a-ma-jig
Rhyming thing-a-ma-jig

A Little Cat, Cat, Cat

A little

 cat

And wore a

hat

Sat on a

mat

And liked to

chat

And the little

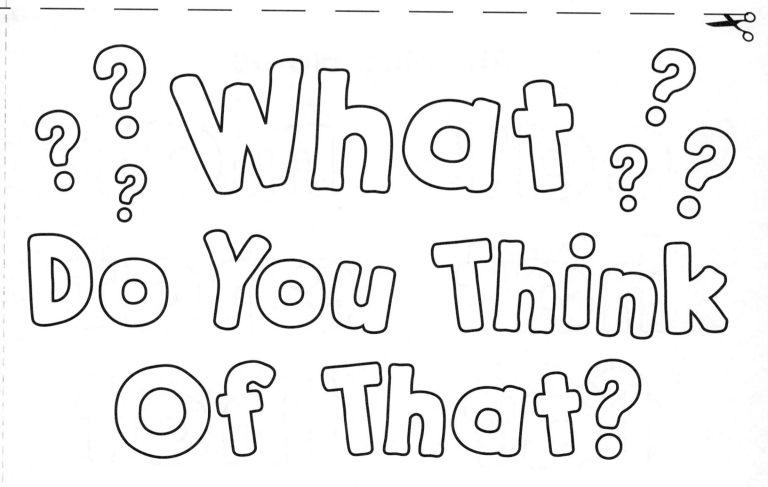

What Do You Think Of That?

Was mighty

Rhyming Words

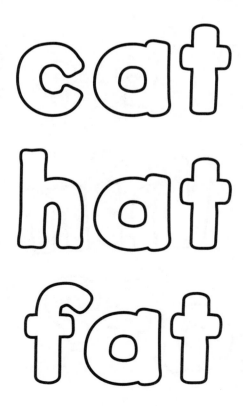

There was a

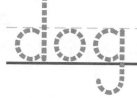

Down by the

Who liked a

Up on a

Now that

dog

14

To see his friend the

frog

Would often

15

Rhyming Words

17

Miss Pretty

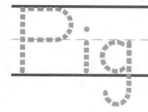

18

While doing the

Wore a

Eating a

Now Pretty

Pig

22

Can you really

dig?

24

Said it's her

Rhyming Words

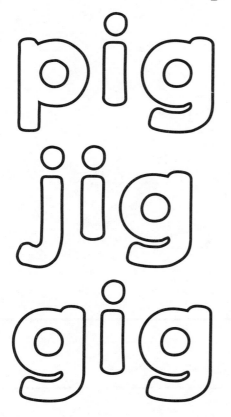

Now little

And the

On the

mat

That liked the

frog

And Miss

Pig

30

It's a rhyming

thing-a-ma-jig

32

Who wore a

wig

31

Rhyming
Thing-a-ma-jig

33

Write Your Own Rhyming Story

These are the rhyming words I will use in my story.

My Friends

Draw a picture of you and your friends.

My friends are

and

We like to play

My friends are nice and

The Best Part

Listen to a story. Draw your favorite part of the story.

The part I liked best was

_____

_____

_____

_____

 Remember to end with a punctuation mark!

Recess Is Fun!

Draw your favorite thing to do at recess.

My favorite thing to do at recess is

I play with

About Me

My name is
_____

_____

My address is
_____

_____

_____

_____

I can call _____ if I need help.

Sing the song "**Call 9-1-1**" to learn how to get help in an emergency.
Download it for free by going to **www.downloadkidsmusic.com**.
Go to page 3 for the promo code.

Phone Number

My phone number is...

☐ ☐ ☐ - ☐ ☐ ☐ - ☐ ☐ ☐ ☐

Write it again...

☐ ☐ ☐ - ☐ ☐ ☐ - ☐ ☐ ☐ ☐

I live with

_____

_____

_____

_____

I have a pet (or I would like to have a pet)

_____

_____

_____

_____

⭐ Remember to end with a punctuation mark!